Design Planning for Freestanding Ambulatory Care Facilities

A Primer for Health Care Providers and Architects

Bill Rostenberg

 American Hospital Publishing, Inc.,
a wholly owned subsidiary of the
American Hospital Association

The views expressed by the author are not necessarily those of the American Hospital Association.

This book is based on a study for the 1983-1984 American Hospital Association-American Institute of Architects Graduate Fellowship in Health Facility Design.

Library of Congress Cataloging-in-Publication Data
Rostenberg, Bill.
  Design planning for freestanding ambulatory care facilities.

  "Catalog no. 043181"—T.p. verso.
  Bibliography: p.
  1. Clinics—Planning.   2. Clinics—Design and
construction.   3. Ambulatory medical care.   I. Title.
[DNLM: 1. Ambulatory Care Facilities.   2. Facility
Design and Construction.   3. Health Facility Planning.
WX 140 R839d]
RA966.R67   1986   725'.5   86-17241
ISBN 0-939450-95-X

Catalog no. 043181

Printed in the U.S.A.
Text set in Helvetica Light.
2.5M-1/87-0145

Karen Downing, Assistant Editor
Beryl Dwight, Editor
Peggy DuMais, Production Coordinator
Brian Schenk, Editorial and Acquisitions Manager, Books
Dorothy Saxner, Vice-President, Books

To my parents, Walter and Hanni Rostenberg, for encouraging me to always ask questions and for teaching me how to find answers.

Contents

About the Author

Bill Rostenberg, AIA, is a registered architect and health facilities planner with Kaplan/McLaughlin/Diaz Architects and Planners in San Francisco. Experienced in master planning, facility planning, space programming, and design development of both acute care hospitals and ambulatory care facilities, Mr. Rostenberg has also seen the user's viewpoint of such facilities as a certified emergency medical technician.

In 1983 Mr. Rostenberg was awarded the Graduate Fellowship in Health Facility Design by the American Hospital Association and the American Institute of Architects. His research on freestanding ambulatory care facilities for that fellowship provided the foundation for this book.

As a member of the American Institute of Architects' Committee on Architecture for Health, Mr. Rostenberg has been active in their Programming and Strategic and Facility Masterplanning Subcommittees. He is also a member of the American Association for Hospital Planning.

List of Figures

Foreword

Design Planning for Freestanding Ambulatory Care Facilities takes a decidedly positive outlook toward opportunities to create buildings that respond to the functional and economic needs of facility owners as well as the health care needs of patients. It suggests that, through adequate planning and design, a project can attain a cost-effective balance between flexibility for future change, efficient use of space, and economy of construction systems and at the same time respond to the market's demands for positive facility image and appropriate amenities. It also considers the many reasons for building a particular facility, from expanding existing markets to diversifying into new markets to avoiding stringent requirements for the costly operation of facilities within a hospital.

The tide is moving relentlessly toward the "unbundling" of alternative delivery and payment systems and the unprecedented growth of ambulatory care. In turn there will be a need for diverse and generally smaller building projects that can respond to a variety of programs, locations, and forms of ownership. Because of this variety, the nature of the owner or client for whom a facility is planned is also changing rapidly: the owner may be one person or several, physician or nonphysician, hospital-affiliated or not. He or she is no longer necessarily a hospital administrator with years of building-planning experience.

There is great latitude in the area of ambulatory care, so much so that many facilities will fail because of duplication of services, incomplete market analyses, poor management, unattainable efficiencies, and inappropriate planning or design. In certain cases the private-profit motive (which has been a major positive force toward decentralization) may tip the scales of planning and decision making in favor of cost efficiency but to the detriment of health care delivery for some patients.

Design Planning for Freestanding Ambulatory Care Facilities is both a primer and a source for more detailed information, which may become necessary as a project proceeds through the usual planning stages. It is the first step for anyone considering the planning, building, financing, or operating of an ambulatory care center. It establishes a common vocabulary for the potential members of a planning team—the owner, the users, and the architect; it raises most of the major issues the planning process must address; and it refers the reader to more extensive information and methodologies for planning from other sources.

James R. Diaz, AIA
San Francisco
June 1986

Preface

The Changing Marketplace

Health care delivery is undergoing revolutionary change. Large institutional providers who for decades were accustomed to treating captive audiences are now encountering a new breed of entrepreneur—providers catering to the wants of an educated, value-conscious market. At the same time, diagnostic services are becoming more advanced, accurate, accessible, and cost-effective. Treatment modalities are less invasive, more oriented toward early prevention of illness, and more dependent on patient participation. The focus of health care delivery is rapidly shifting toward outpatient and home care, while at the same time venture capital for costly equipment and construction is vanishing, becoming the object of fierce competition.

Perhaps the most dramatic change in health care is that payment systems have become prospective, rather than retrospective, in an attempt to cap escalating reimbursement costs. Because the health care industry touches every aspect of our economy, no one is immune from its effects.

This transformation is driven by pressures influencing regulators, providers, and consumers. Legislators, confronted with unprecedented mandates to contain health care costs, have implemented national prospective pricing systems (PPS) designed to limit medical service charges. As a result, physicians are finding they must supplement their medical educations with business savvy, and hospitals are attempting both "beat 'em" and "join 'em" strategies. Many are entering into cooperative business arrangements with other hospitals and with physician groups in order to maintain their market interests.

Another notable change is the change in the consumer. As health care has become accepted as a marketable commodity, the consumer, out of necessity, has become better educated and more choice-conscious. As a result, marketing strategies and facility image are now significant criteria by which the consumer chooses services.

Forces of Change

The health care revolution is being fueled by three primary forces: (1) cost containment policies, (2) new technologies, and (3) increased competition in the health care marketplace.

Cost Containment

Diagnosis-related groups (DRGs) are individual elements of a federally regulated price list that limits the dollar amount providers are reimbursed for treating specific medical conditions. Because each condition or DRG corresponds to a fixed reimbursement price, rather than actual treatment costs, practitioners are given financial incentives to tighten their treatment budgets, often by reducing the number and length of hospital admissions. As a result, the industry is seeing a dramatic increase in outpatient treatment, much of which occurs in nonhospital settings.

Many providers are finding that well-managed, properly designed freestanding facilities can lower both initial capital outlays (because of nonhospital-type construction) and operating expenses (when efficient staffing is used) compared to similar in-hospital facilities.

New Technologies

Although reimbursement policies are becoming more rigid, medical research and technological development continues. This is affecting the utilization of freestanding outpatient centers in a variety of ways.

First, independent or small group providers can now afford more powerful, sophisticated equipment and therefore provide a wider range of services than before. Some diagnostic and treatment equipment previously too large and/or too costly for single practitioners to own is now smaller and less expensive. In addition, processes are being developed that allow diagnostic instruments, such as chemical analyzers, to perform tests more rapidly and at a lower cost than before. Instruments are "user friendly"; many no longer require specially trained technicians to operate them.

Second, diagnostic imaging is a profitable autonomous service. The growing demand for early diagnosis, coupled with technological versatility, has enabled small group practitioners to compete with hospitals for imaging services. Preventive approaches to health maintenance continue to increase the demand for easily accessible diagnostic procedures. Radiology, tomography, ultrasound, and magnetic imaging are regularly offered in freestanding settings. Computerized axial tomography (CAT) scanners and magnetic resonance imaging devices, available in mobile-truck-mounted installations, accommodate "time sharing," which reduces individual capital outlay and increases patient accessibility. Advances in imaging capabilities, such as cinematic viewing, enable physicians to observe physiological processes in action, thus increasing the incidence of life-saving and dollar-saving early diagnoses.

Third, medicine has become less invasive. Many procedures that previously required hospitalization are now routinely performed on an outpatient basis, thanks to new non-invasive or less-invasive techniques. Outpatient surgery is common for myriad orthopedic, ophthalmic, gynecological, cardiac, and oncological procedures requiring a minimal recovery period. Arthroscopy allows examination and treatment of joints with only minor incisions. Laser surgery can reduce healing time by minimizing tissue trauma and reducing blood loss. Providing these services in settings that cost less to build and that accommodate patients' desires for convenience and accessibility is prudent.

Competition in the Marketplace

Hospitals and physicians alike are now catering to patients' requests that had previously gone unanswered. "Along with changes in the health market there have come changes in public attitudes. The patient has evolved from a relatively passive player directed by a physician to a better informed, independent consumer" (Quebe 1985, p. 4).

As a greater variety of practitioners compete for their share of the market, the smart ones realize the need for effective architectural packaging of their facilities. As a result, architects and planners are challenged by mandates for extremely cost-effective design coupled with mass appeal and a noninstitutional yet sophisticated image.

Another result of increased competition is the development of "medical malls" that offer both accessibility and convenience to health care shoppers. When the first freestanding health centers were built, most facilities were single-service structures—surgicenters, emergicenters, and so forth. Developers now realize the added convenience, as perceived by patients, of clustering an array of primary and ancillary services within a freestanding structure.

The freestanding ambulatory care facility has evolved as an alternative to large, institutional, hospital-like structures. In many instances the freestanding structure is more desirable than a traditional model. Although a successful health care practice depends primarily on the nonarchitectural aspects of health care delivery, such as qualified personnel, proper management, adequate financing, and appropriate marketing, thorough facility planning and effective design will enable a capable staff to better achieve its goals.

Acknowledgments

Many persons have assisted me in the creation of this book by contributing their time, insights, objective criticism, and resources. My research began through a fellowship granted by the American Hospital Association (AHA) and the American Institute of Architects (AIA) Committee on Architecture for Health. Both organizations enabled me to develop my preliminary findings into this book. In particular, I am grateful for the opportunity to continue my participation in the Committee on Architecture for Health's Programming Subcommittee and Strategic and Facility Masterplanning Subcommittee. I owe special thanks to James R. Diaz, AIA, Solomon S. Pan, AIA, and Joseph G. Sprague, AIA, for their encouragement and support.

During the term of my fellowship I received invaluable assistance and commentary from William Kirby Lockard, FAIA; Douglas J. MacNeil; Kenneth V. Iserson, MD; and Leon Bennet-Alder, at the University of Arizona in Tucson; and also from Darrell P. Thorpe, MD; M. Melissa Rigg; and John Kenney.

My endeavors during the seemingly endless period of revisions that followed were eased by the ingenious insights of Joseph Readdy, Eve Meyer, John Schlesinger, AIA, and the staff of Kaplan/McLaughlin/Diaz Architects and Planners. Special thanks at Kaplan/McLaughlin/Diaz go to James R. Diaz, AIA, Kenneth Schwarz, AIA, Alex Bonutti, AIA, Jeffery Hazard, Bruce Nepp, AIA, Harish Bhatt, Jan Vargo, Annette Gaskin, John Fahey, Jean Hountalas, and Sally Painter.

My wife Debbie, a registered nurse, was responsible for helping me translate the subtleties of an often cryptic medical jargon into a language understandable by laypersons, as well as refocusing my attention away from this book, as necessary, back to the remaining all-too-often-neglected aspects of our lives.

Finally, I am indebted to the staff of American Hospital Publishing, Inc., for their diligence and perseverance in producing this book. Karen Downing edited the major portion of the text and succeeded in restraining an architect's temptation to initiate "just one more revision" on numerous occasions. Beryl Dwight and Rex N. Olsen also edited the manuscript. The manuscript was reviewed by Judith R. Dolgoff, Director of Real Estate Development, Harvard Community Health Plan; Willis Reed, M.D., Phoenix, Arizona; and Annette L. Valenta, Dr.P.H., Director, Department of Facility Planning and Design, AHA. Peggy DuMais was responsible for the book design, layout, and production.

Part I
Purpose and Description of Freestanding Ambulatory Care Facilities

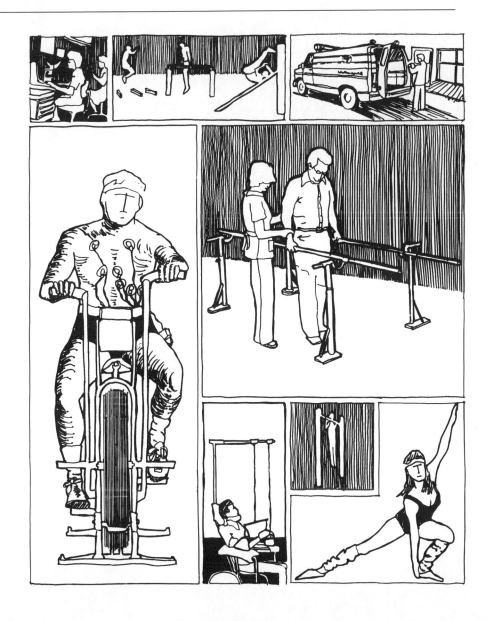

Chapter 1

Introduction

In an attempt to increase their market share, many health care providers have sought new ways to offer services to a convenience-seeking and economy-minded population. One viable nonhospital setting for offering health care services to this value-conscious market is the freestanding ambulatory health care facility. However, these facilities are too often designed as if they were merely office buildings with special utility connections for the medical equipment they house but without any other consideration for their special character and unique place in the health care market.

This book represents a resource for planning freestanding ambulatory health care facilities: buildings that are neither offices nor hospitals but a combination of aspects of both. It describes the limitations of such a facility, identifies the services that it is likely to house, and discusses the design considerations that must be addressed in response to its special character. These considerations include the need to incorporate efficiency, flexibility, and safety while maintaining a separation from backup facilities such as hospitals.

In designing hospitals, the project team typically consists of professionals who are familiar with both architectural and health care planning processes; however, such a team is not always involved in designing freestanding facilities. More and more health care providers, including independent physicians or those in group practice, are developing their own facilities, perhaps with little qualified planning assistance. Similarly, small architectural firms with little or no previous health experience are designing these facilities as a means of entering this new area of the design market. Moreover, project budget limitations often preclude the engagement of large architectural firms that have health care specialists on staff.

Therefore, as a planning resource, this book is designed to help health care providers and designers learn about each other's needs and procedures. A successful design solution results from an accurate transformation of the providers' needs into a functional and aesthetically satisfying building.

For those health care providers not yet fluent in the process of designing a health care facility, this book provides them the opportunity to learn about architectural programming and design processes so they can provide better data to the architect. For architects, it explains how to apply general programmatic concepts specifically to the design of ambulatory care facilities.

The book identifies information that must be known prior to the design process but does not suggest any one particular design solution. The intent is not to provide all the answers needed to design an ambulatory care facility, but rather to assist the project team in learning what essential questions need to be asked prior to design.

In summary, the book is directed to an interdisciplinary group of health care providers, administrators, planners, and architects. It focuses mainly on providing information to those persons not yet well-versed in the process of designing health care facilities, but it is also useful to veteran health care architects as a comprehensive checklist of relevant issues regarding the design of freestanding ambulatory facilities.

Chapter **2**

Defining Freestanding Ambulatory Care Facilities

In the past two decades, changes in consumer attitudes toward health care, the rapid development of new technologies, and the spiraling cost of providing medical services to the community have produced dramatic changes in the delivery of health care services. One of the most obvious results of these changes has been increased use of ambulatory care facilities.

Rather than serving merely as an adjunct to institution-based inpatient services, the ambulatory care facility of today represents a unique level of health care. It is clear that its role is and will continue to be one of providing health care alternatives to all facets of the community while challenging more traditional providers to respond in kind.

These changes in delivery systems have led to the popularity of new types of medical practitioners, such as physician extenders, and to the development of such new facility types as freestanding ambulatory care centers.

For the purposes of this book, a freestanding ambulatory care facility is defined as any building that is not physically attached to a hospital and in which medical and/or health care services are offered to ambulatory persons. This definition is intentionally broad to include a large variety

of services ranging from those offered by technically equipped ambulatory surgery centers at one end of the spectrum to nonmedical fitness centers at the other.

Freestanding facilities provide a range of diagnostic, treatment, and health maintenance services both to communities where few medical facilities are located and to areas where many ambulatory services exist but are less accessible because of limited hours of operation or long waiting lines. The freestanding ambulatory care facility is ideally suited to areas where additional health services are needed but where the duplication of large-scale hospitals is not warranted or feasible.

Freestanding ambulatory care programs are structured in many ways. They may be controlled by a hospital completely, partially, or not at all. A facility that a hospital governs, manages, and finances is hospital-sponsored. A center that a hospital "governs and manages, but that is financed through a contractual arrangement between the hospital and physicians concerning program revenue and expenses is hospital-associated" (Burns and Ferber 1981, p. 73). A facility that has no organizational ties to a hospital is independent.

Limits of the Freestanding Facility

Combining a variety of ambulatory care services within a single freestanding structure might appear to result in nothing more than a small hospital with limited capabilities. This, however, is not the case. The freestanding ambulatory care facility is designed for a special purpose—to improve patient access to specific services, to increase market share, and to reduce costly operational overhead. In addition, construction costs often can be substantially reduced if the building can be classified as not having inpatient occupancy. The following three categories define the limits of the ambulatory care facility and thereby differentiate it from a hospital (figure 1).

Time of Need

Although many services of the facility may be offered around the clock, others are likely to be available on a limited basis. Urgent care, for example, might be offered seven days a week from 7 a.m. to 10 p.m. Patients requiring this service at 2 a.m. would therefore be referred to some other facility, such as a hospital emergency department, even though their problem might not require emergency services.

Equipment and/or Personnel Needs

Because of the limited scope of the freestanding facility, both its staff and its medical capabilities are less extensive than those of a hospital. For this reason, it is equipped to accommodate patient needs that are routine and relatively uncomplicated. For example, it may not have the sophisticated emergency backup capabilities that a hospital does. Its surgical

Figure 1. Limits of the Freestanding Facility

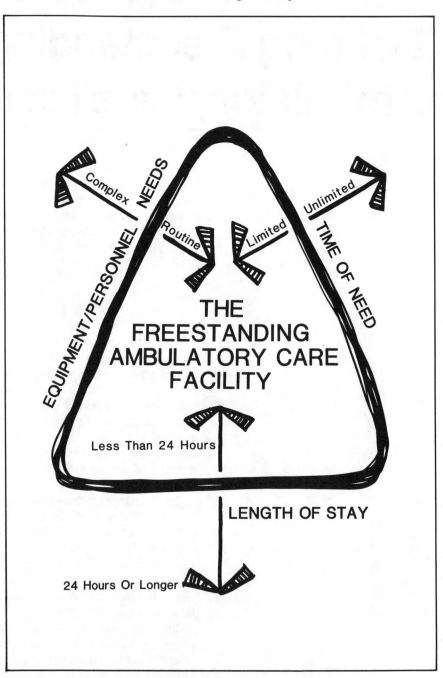

The freestanding ambulatory care facility is best suited for routine procedures, for which overnight observation is not required.

capabilities also are limited, and such items as whole blood may not be immediately available. Therefore, high-risk patients may be referred to a hospital for some types of treatment, depending on their condition.

Length of Stay

Any facility designed to treat patients whose stay is normally less than 24 hours is classified as having an ambulatory occupancy and may be subject to less stringent code requirements than is a facility that treats overnight patients. The regulatory process for an ambulatory facility is likely to be less lengthy and costly than that for an inpatient facility. One exception to this classification is the ambulatory facility designed to occasionally hold a patient for 24-hour observation. Eligibility for this exception should be verified by the governing regulatory agencies, however, as this and other code requirements vary by locale.

Types of Services

The possible range of services that a freestanding facility might offer includes almost any health-related service that does not require the support of a hospital or its staff. It may be helpful to consider these services in the categories shown in figure 2 and discussed below.

Although it is not expected that any one ambulatory care facility will include services in all of these categories, the combining of services should be considered when a combination will reduce initial and/or operating costs and also will not sacrifice the efficiency or quality of any of the services being provided.

Immediate Care

Immediate care is the treatment of urgent, but not life-threatening, injuries or illnesses. Such services often are available with extended hours,

sometimes 24 hours a day. Usually, the cases are episodic, and follow-up care generally is not provided at the place of initial treatment. The facility, sometimes called an urgent care center, is not intended to receive patients transported by ambulance, nor is it typically equipped to treat such medical emergencies as heart attacks or strokes.

Some facilities providing immediate care are known as freestanding emergency centers or "emergicenters." This nomenclature is considered inappropriate by many because the word *emergency* has a unique connotation and can be misleading to the patient who is brought to such a facility in need of staff and equipment capabilities greater than those that actually exist. It is extremely important that the public not confuse the emergicenter, regardless of its capabilities, with an emergency department or a trauma center (figure 3).

Figure 2. Types of Services

Immediate Care
  Emergency treatment
  Urgent care

Primary Care
  Family practice
  Industrial medicine
  Pediatrics

Intermediate Care
  Ambulatory surgery
  Birthing
  Clinical laboratory
  Imaging (radiology, nuclear medicine,
    and other imaging techniques)
  Radiation therapy

Posthospital Care
  Physical therapy
  Occupational therapy
  Recreational therapy
  Sports medicine
  Cardiac rehabilitation
  Substance abuse treatment
  Counseling

Preventive Care
  Physical fitness
  Education
  Counseling

Ancillary services
  Pharmacy
  Durable medical equipment sales
  Miscellaneous retail functions
    (coffee shop, for example)

Figure 3. Immediate Care

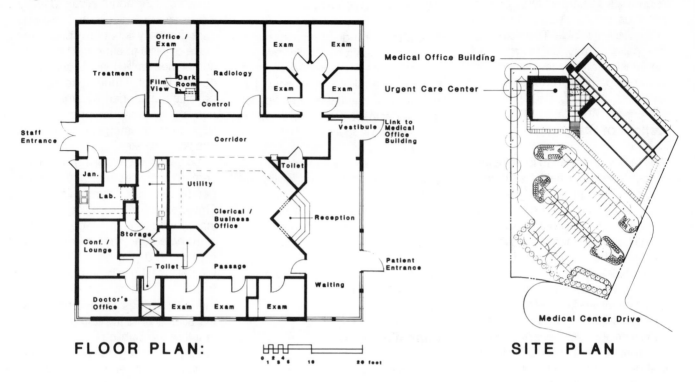

FLOOR PLAN:

SITE PLAN

Morgan Hill Urgent Care Center exemplifies the immediate care setting. Note its proximity to primary care practitioners in the adjacent medical office building. (Reprinted with the permission of Kaplan/McLaughlin/Diaz Architects and Planners, ©1986. Photo by Sally Painter.)

Primary Care

Primary care refers to general practice (basic or general health care), the point at which a person first seeks assistance from the health care system. Primary care is the most flexible area of the total health care system, requiring the least equipment and having the greatest ability to extend to even the outermost fringes of the community. Primary care patients are referred to secondary or tertiary care specialists if their condition so warrants.

Primary care usually is provided on a scheduled basis and routinely includes follow-up care. Traditionally, its availability has been limited to regular business hours, with the result that patients inappropriately rely on hospital emergency departments for expensive after-hours nonemergency visits. In recent years, however, extended-hours practices have become both common and profitable.

The typical freestanding primary care setting is similar to a family practice or group practice office, usually with good public visibility (figure 4).

Mills Medical Arts Building attracts a variety of primary care practitioners. Its bold atrium entrance and proximity to Mills Hospital are strong selling points. (Reprinted with the permission of Kaplan/McLaughlin/Diaz Architects and Planners, ©1986. Photo by Charles Callister.)

Figure 4. Primary Care

EXTERIOR AT ATRIUM

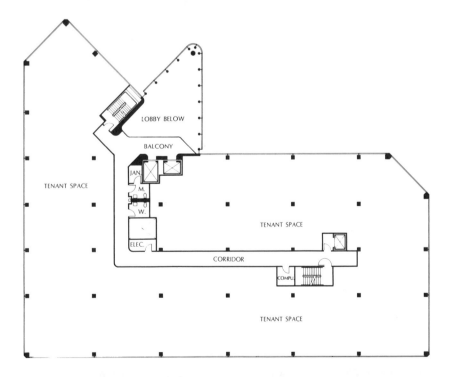

TYPICAL FLOOR PLAN – Medical Arts Building

Intermediate Care

Intermediate care refers to services for patients whose condition requires specialized equipment or specially trained personnel yet is not of such consequence that they must be admitted as hospital inpatients. Both diagnostic and treatment procedures may be offered as part of intermediate care. Examples include ambulatory surgery, diagnostic imaging, and radiation therapy.

The freestanding surgical center typifies the intermediate care setting. It is designed for procedures with a relatively short recovery time (those that do not require overnight observation) and a low risk of immediate complication, and for patients who are both willing and able to recover at home (figure 5).

Posthospital Care

Posthospital care includes a variety of services rendered after hospitalization, disease, or traumatic injury, usually involving both physical and psychological aspects of rehabilitation. These services include physical, recreational, and occupational therapy; cardiac rehabilitation; and sports medicine (figure 6).

Figure 5. Intermediate Care

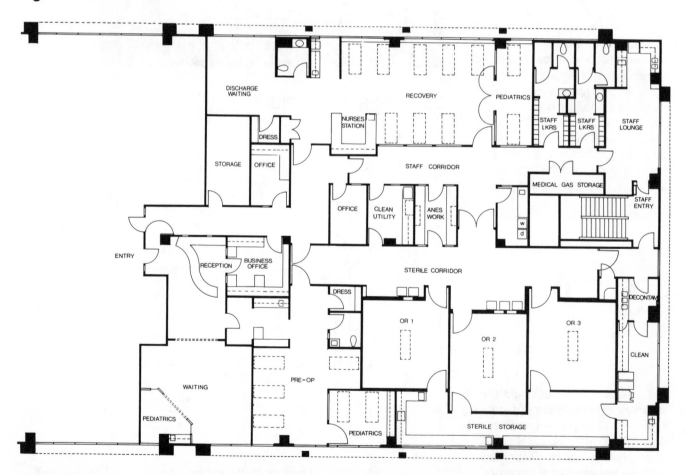

Stoneridge Surgical Center was designed to occupy space within a preexisting medical office building. In such cases, it is important that the size, location, and configuration of available space be appropriate to the project's needs. (Reprinted with the permission of Kaplan/McLaughlin/Diaz Architects and Planners, ©1986.)

Figure 6. Posthospital Care

Active Care Sports and Chronic Injury Center is an affiliate of French Hospital in San Francisco. Deep structural bays provide an expansive and unobstructed space that is conducive to a variety of equipment layouts. (Reprinted with the permission of French Hospital. Photo by Sally Painter.)

A rapidly increasing market also exists for substance-abuse treatment. Although these programs often take place in specially designed inpatient facilities, portions of this treatment, such as counseling and follow-up care, can be given on an outpatient basis. Such outpatient services are of particular value to persons who require treatment but who want to remain involved in daily life activities that inpatient confinement would preclude.

Preventive Care

Preventive care services include education, fitness, and such preventive measures as periodic health examinations, multiphasic screening, and immunization programs. The ideal facility includes classrooms, examination rooms, a library, and a variety of exercise spaces, but an adequate program can be operated in a single multipurpose room.

Many primary care and immediate care providers offer educational and fitness activities as a marketing tool to increase both their public exposure and their market share of services. Also, providers of prepaid health care, such as health maintenance organizations (HMOs), offer preventive services to reduce the likelihood that their members will require more costly treatment later on.

Ancillary Services

Health care services in freestanding facilities serve a slightly different function than the same services in a hospital setting. For example, the radiology department in a hospital traditionally has been considered an ancillary service; however, in an ambulatory care setting, radiology services might be the primary focus of the facility. Therefore, for the purposes of this book, "ancillary services" are defined as retail services that support the diagnostic and treatment services described above, such as the sale of pharmaceuticals, orthotics (mechanical orthopedic appliances), or other therapeutic devices. Ancillary services may serve patients directly or indirectly through referral from a diagnostic or treatment area.

Accreditation and Regulation

Accreditation and regulation requirements for freestanding ambulatory care facilities vary from state to state. They are generally determined by the building's location, occupancy classification, extent of services, form of ownership, and by the political climate of the time. In some jurisdictions, the building may be regarded as a physician's office and therefore be virtually unregulated. In other instances, certain requirements concerning both construction and operations must be met.

National requirements and uniform definitions do not exist for facilities providing immediate care, but many local and professional organizations have developed their own guidelines. Although guidelines that are applicable on a national level may have no legal authority unless they are adopted by some local regulatory agency, planners are well advised to become aware of all such guidelines. One such example is the American Medical Association's suggested criteria for any facility that uses the word *emergency* in its name. The criteria include availability of services 24 hours a day every day of the year, as well as minimum staffing requirements.

In 1973, the Joint Commission on Accreditation of Hospitals (JCAH) published its first standards for ambulatory care services. These were written primarily for hospital outpatient departments. "In 1976, JCAH began its accreditation process for freestanding facilities. One-third of the ambulatory health care organizations accredited by JCAH are affiliated with hospitals; the remainder are freestanding. Facilities are evaluated according to the standards contained in the *Accreditation Manual for Ambulatory Health Care,* published by JCAH" (JCAH Ambulatory Health Care Standards Manual, 1986).

JCAH accreditation is a voluntary process based on peer evaluation. Some states do, however, require that JCAH standards be met for certain ambulatory facilities, such as outpatient surgery and emergency centers, before licensure is granted.

Certificate of Need

Some states require that the owner of a proposed freestanding (or any other) health care facility submit an application to local governing agencies substantiating the need for such a facility. In theory, the purpose of the certificate of need (CON) is to reduce unnecessary duplication of expensive equipment and services, the cost of which would ultimately be passed on to the public. Because the regulatory agency has the authority to deny certification if it finds that a proposal is not in the best interest of the community, an experienced architectural consultant can be of great value during the review process.

Ironically, the costs involved in the review process, both in dollars and in time, often make facility costs higher than they would have been without such certification. Another problem with the CON process is that CON requirements apply differently under different sets of circumstances. For example, a hospital-owned ambulatory surgery center may require a CON, while an identical facility owned and operated by an independent surgeon may be exempt. This situation has led many providers to search for loopholes in the statutes or to seek exemption, often by legally establishing the facility in the name of an independent provider. Many state legislatures, recognizing the problems with the CON process, have chosen to revise their statutes or to drop them altogether.

Linkages to Backup Facilities

The extent and types of services to be included in the freestanding ambulatory care facility will be, in part, the result of an in-depth market analysis of both the general region and the specific locality in which the facility is to be developed. Before this analysis is prepared, two very important questions must be asked: Who are the initiators of the project? What do they expect to gain from the facility's existence? The building or buildings may be owned or sponsored by a hospital, a health maintenance organization (HMO), independent physicians, or by some third party such as a private management corporation. It is important to note that each has a different system for delivering health care services and different reasons for and expectations in developing a freestanding facility.

As competition in the health care marketplace escalates, many providers are decentralizing their services to make them more accessible to the public. The freestanding satellite facility offers the opportunity for a system to expand its catchment area and provide a greater variety of services.

The relationship of the satellite to a centralized backup facility is determined by the marketing objectives of the system (hospital, HMO, and so forth). A hospital, for example, might establish a satellite in order to generate referrals to the hospital by making its presence known in a new demographic area. In this arrangement, the relationship between the satellite and the backup facility is one of a gateway directing patients to the center of the system.

An HMO, as a prepaid provider, wants to restrict access to cost-intensive services, while ensuring that its facilities will meet the demands of its membership. Unlike the hospital, the HMO system is designed to minimize the transfer of subscribers from one facility to another. This is usually accomplished by establishing a series of satellite facilities, each with its own distinct catchment area.

A facility owned by private physicians or other independent health care providers is likely to be smaller than one established by a hospital or an HMO. Rather than offer the wide range of services that the other groups provide, this facility reflects the specialties of its organizers. The independent freestanding facility represents the nucleus of its system, with referrals occurring only when its capabilities are exceeded.

Each of these three distinct systems illustrates a different relationship between the satellite and its backup facility. The hospital-based system promotes referrals, the HMO reduces the incidence of referrals, and the independent facility provides referrals only when emergency backup is required (figure 7).

The identification of the relationship between the freestanding facility and the health care delivery system within which it exists is integral to planning the project. The facility owner's strategy for supporting or competing with other health care providers will influence market analyses, projections of anticipated facility utilization, site selection, and design criteria.

Figure 7. Linkages to Backup Facilities

HOSPITAL
SYSTEM

HEALTH
MAINTENANCE
ORGANIZATION

INDEPENDENT
SYSTEM

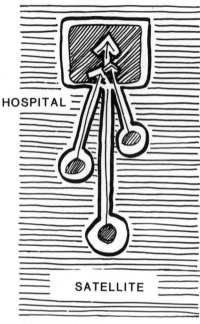

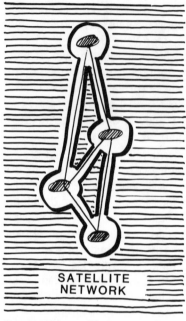

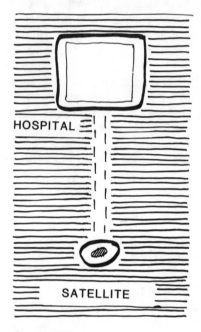

Individual
Satellites
Promote
Referrals

Satellite Network
Reduces
The Incidence Of
Referrals To Others

Satellite
Linked To Hospital
For
Emergency Support

The relationship between a satellite and its backup facility varies with the delivery system within which it exists.

Part II

The Planning Process

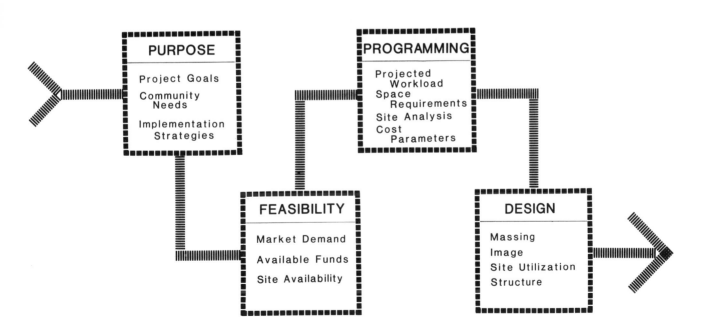

PURPOSE

Project Goals

Community Needs

Implementation Strategies

PROGRAMMING

Projected Workload
Space Requirements
Site Analysis
Cost Parameters

FEASIBILITY

Market Demand

Available Funds

Site Availability

DESIGN

Massing
Image
Site Utilization
Structure

Chapter **3**

Project Goals
and the Project Team

A project team should be organized as soon as a project is initiated. Members of the project team should identify their reasons for initiating the project before specific planning tasks are undertaken. Project goals and feasibility must be clarified before the team can proceed with architectural programming and design.

Goals

Project goals must satisfy existing community needs. For example, *affordable health care* might be a community need. *Increased market share* might be one goal of the project team. The strategy of offering diagnostic and treatment services during extended hours might provide both affordable health care for the community and an increased market share for the provider, thus fulfilling the project goal by satisfying a community need.

Strategies for achieving project goals are implemented by the project team. The team players include the owner, the architect, and a variety of consultants. Because each

player's expertise and interests will vary at different phases of the project, it is of paramount importance that individual goals give way to collective project goals, which should be clearly defined early on.

Each goal should reflect and support the underlying purpose of the project. Ideally, the goals will state a philosophy of delivering health care services, meeting community needs, and capturing future and existing markets. For example, a freestanding hospital-owned diagnostic center proposed for a rapidly growing suburb outside the hospital's service area might have the following goals:

- Provide convenient and accessible diagnostic services
- Attract qualified physicians and staff to become affiliated with the hospital
- Expand the hospital's service area
- Preempt competition by providing services previously unavailable in the market area

Once the goals have been stated, planning and design decisions can be guided by the project team's initial objectives or mission statement.

When establishing goals, it is important to consider *what is to be achieved* before determining *how it is to be accomplished*. If goals are stated in terms of a physical solution, opportunities will be limited, and the purpose of clarifying objectives will be defeated.

Team Members

The composition of the team will change as the project progresses. For example, marketing consultants are invaluable for feasibility studies, in the early stages of the project, whereas structural engineers are needed later, during facility design. Consequently, individual responsibilities for achieving project goals should be clarified as each new member joins the team. The project owner should consider designating one individual as having overall responsibility for directing the team.

Owner

The owner is the individual or group responsible for initiating the project, guiding it through the planning process, funding it, and maintaining the facility throughout its useful life. He or she should be represented on the team by capable persons who are authorized to make timely decisions, inasmuch as they will have major responsibilities at every phase of the project. If the owner is a hospital, it is likely to be represented by an administrator or a key staff member. If a physician is the owner, his or her partners are likely to be the team representatives. If the owner is represented by many people, it is crucial that they as a group develop a workable decision-making process.

The owner's representatives should include both managers and users.

(In this context, "users" refers to staff rather than patients.) The user tends to be concerned with ease of operation, whereas the manager tends to be primarily concerned with budgetary constraints. A successful project team will try to satisfy the needs of both groups.

Architect

The architect is a facilitator whose chief charge is to simultaneously accommodate (1) the needs and wishes of the owner, (2) the technology of construction, and (3) the realities of the environment. Needless to say, this must all be accomplished within the owner's stated means and within regulatory limitations. The architect also must compile meaningful data by decoding information furnished by the owner and the consultants.

During the construction phase, the architect may be responsible for advising and consulting with the owner regarding administration of the construction contract. However, the owner will often hire a construction manager to supervise actual construction, as distinct from administering the construction contract.

Consultant

Consultant is that magic word that describes the person or persons who have the ability to do what the owner and architect cannot. Consultants may not be necessary if the project is relatively uncomplicated, the owner is experienced in facility development, and the architect is familiar with the facility type. However, a consultant may provide a valuable second opinion, particularly if the owner has not previously worked with the architect.

Consultants may be engaged for

any facet of the project, from financing to landscaping. Some consultants may be hired directly by the owner (marketing and legal advisers, for example), while others, such as mechanical and structural engineers, work indirectly for the owner through an agreement (contract) between themselves and the architect.

Generally, the consultant gives guidance during determination of need, organization, and operation, whereas the architect takes the lead when it comes time to translate these elements into physical plans (Rea et al. 1978, p. 3).

Responsibilities of Team Members

The American Institute of Architects (AIA) has developed a series of standard documents to guide both architects and their clients through the planning and construction processes. These documents, which are based on court-tested concepts, are intended to clarify the legal responsibilities of the parties involved, in order to protect the owner as well as the architect. The documents may be modified, by mutual consent of the parties, to fit the special requirements of a particular project.

AIA Document B141, *Standard Form of Agreement between Owner and Architect,* is recognized as an industry standard that defines both basic and additional architectural services. Basic services consist of five phases of work:

1. Schematic design phase
2. Design development phase
3. Construction documents phase
4. Bidding or negotiation phase
5. Construction phase—administration of the construction contract

Additional services, as described in AIA Document B141, include but are not limited to the following (AIA Doc. B141 1977, p. 5):

- Providing analyses of the owner's needs and programming the requirements of the project
- Providing financial feasibility or other special studies
- Providing planning surveys, site evaluations, environmental studies, or comparative studies of prospective sites; preparing special surveys, studies, and submissions required for approvals of governmental authorities or others having jurisdiction over the project
- Providing services relative to future facilities, systems, and equipment that are not intended to be constructed during the construction phase
- Providing interior design and other similar services required for or in connection with the selection, procurement, or installation of furniture, furnishings, and related equipment
- Providing services of consultants for other than the normal architectural, structural, mechanical, and electrical engineering services of the project

If additional services are requested by the owner, additional compensation may be in order, depending on the exact language of the agreement between the parties.

Figure 8 illustrates the major responsibilities of the primary project team members at various phases of the project (adapted from Rea et al. 1978, p. 4).

Figure 8. Project Phases and Responsibilities of Project Team Members

Project Phase	Description	Responsibility		
		Owner	Consultant	Architect
Organization	1. Initiate project.	X		
	2. Select planning team members.	X		
Predesign	3. Conduct market survey; establish community needs.	X	X	
	4. Define provider's role, clarify project goals.	X	X	
	5. Obtain financial feasibility study from independent source.	X	O	O (A)
	6. Prepare functional and spatial programs.	O	X	O (A)
	7. Prepare preliminary budget.	X	O	O (A)
	8. Select site.	X	O	O (A)
Schematic Design	9. Evaluate preliminary programs and budget.	O	O	X (B1)
	10. Prepare schematic and preliminary plans.	O	O	X (B1)
	11. Develop statement of probable construction costs.	O	O	X (B1)
Design Development	12. Prepare site development plan.	O	O	X (B2)
	13. Secure all preliminary agency approvals.	X	O	O (B2)
	14. Develop further statement of probable construction costs.	O	O	X (B2)

Figure 8 illustrates the sequence of project phases and the major responsibilities of the primary project team members. (Adapted from *Building a Hospital: A Primer for Administrators,* by Rea et al. ©1978 by American Hospital Publishing, Inc.)

Figure 8. Project Phases and Responsibilities of Project Team Members (continued)

Project Phase	Description	Responsibility		
		Owner	Consultant	Architect
Construction Documents	15. Prepare working drawings and specifications.	O	O	X (B3)
	16. Develop further statement of probable construction costs.	O	O	X (B3)
	17. Secure all agency approvals.	X	O	O (B3)
	18. Prepare bid package.	X	O	X (B3)
Bidding or Negotiating	19. Take bids.	X	O	O (B4)
	20. Complete financing.	X	O	
Construction	21. Award contracts.	X	O	O (B5)
	22. Administer construction contract.			X (B5)
	23. Handle construction payments.	X		O (B5)
	24. Develop equipment list and specifications.	X	O	O (A)
	25. Purchase equipment.	X		

SYMBOL KEY

X	Leadership role
O	Secondary, consulting, or assisting role
A	Additional service*
B1	Basic schematic design service*
B2	Basic design development service*
B3	Basic construction documents service*
B4	Basic bidding and/or negotiating service*
B5	Basic construction contract administration service*

*As described in AIA doc. B141

Chapter 4

The Programming Process

Before beginning architectural design, the project team must initiate a series of investigative activities, which identify the client's needs and translate them into design criteria. These activities constitute what is known as *architectural programming*. Although one universally accepted definition of programming does not exist, it can be thought of as "a process of identifying and defining the design needs of a facility and communicating the requirements of the [owner] to the designer" (Palmer 1981, p. 7). The end product of this process, the architectural program, is a planning tool that can be as useful to the owner as it is to the architect.

Types of Programs

There are many types of architectural programs, each dealing with a specific type of data (space, function, circulation, massing, mechanical systems, structure, and so forth). Most programs are written in such a way that they consolidate and simplify operational data and present it in a form that is usable by the designer without suggesting a particular design solution. Some types of programs are more useful than others for individual design decisions.

In *The Architect's Guide to Facility Programming,* Palmer describes three kinds of architectural programs (figure 9):

The master program *defines design issues relating to the overall scope of the project. It identifies and outlines the principal issues, defines goals and establishes the limits of the program. It enables the owner to determine project feasibility, estimate a preliminary budget and comprehend initial schematic design alternatives.*

The facility program *supplies a base for designing all the primary components and the integrated total of the facility and for evaluation of design process (for example, verifying area and volume calculations).*

The component program *is the most specific of the three levels and relates directly to the most specific design detailing. It provides precise requirements*

Figure 9. Types of Architectural Programs

Design Decision	Master	Facility	Component
Site selection	X	O	
Economic feasibility	X	O	
Functional feasibility	X	O	
Design feasibility	X	O	
Project budget	X	X	X
Project schedule	X	X	X
Geometric proportions	X	X	O
Configuration	O	X	O
Orientation	X	O	
Site plan	X	X	
Sitework plan	O	X	O
Massing plan	O	X	O
Envelope design		X	O
Gross volume calculation	O	X	O
Gross area calculation	O	X	O
Net area calculation	O	X	O
Circulation area calculation		X	O
Space unit area calculation		X	X
Space unit design		O	X
Floor plan layout		X	X
Space layout		X	O
Circulation design		X	O
Operations design		X	X
Design energy budget	O	X	O
Engineering systems selection	O	X	
Engineering systems design			X

Figure 9 identifies the type of architectural program that is most appropriate for each of several design decisions. (Reprinted, with permission, from *The Architect's Guide to Facility Programming*, by Palmer. © 1981 by The American Institute of Architects. Permission no. 86032. Further reproduction is prohibited.)

Figure 9. Types of Architectural Programs (continued)

Design Decision	Master	Facility	Component
Nonengineering systems selection	O	X	
Nonengineering systems design			X
Lighting systems selection	O	X	
Lighting systems design			X
Structural design		X	O
Support service design		O	X
Fenestration		O	X
Designed energy performance		X	O
Landscape design		X	X
Code compliance	O	X	X
Project cost estimate		X	O
Construction cost estimate		X	O
Operating cost estimate		O	X
Life cycle cost estimate		X	X
Construction schedule	O	X	O
Economic analysis	O	X	O
Solar system sizing		O	X
Construction materials selection		X	X
Exterior finishes		O	X
Interior finishes		O	X
Equipment furnishing selection		O	X

X = primary usefulness of information to design decision
O = secondary usefulness of information to design decision

for design of individual compo-nents of the facility, such as the various engineering systems and the individual space units. The component program also most specifically reflects the needs of the individual facility users (adapted from Palmer 1981, p. 23).

Two aspects of programming that must precede design planning are *functional programming* and *spatial programming*. The functional program evaluates levels of patient utilization, such as projected work load data—anticipated procedures per year and average duration of procedures. The end product of functional programming is a description of the requirements of each service (surgery, for example) in terms of staffing, equipment, and circulation.

Spatial programming translates the functional program into area requirements. The spatial program tabulates size, quantity, and spatial characteristics for every room or department. Functional programming precedes spatial programming, and spatial programming precedes design planning.

Relationship of Programming to Design

Opinions vary regarding the precise point at which programming ends and design begins. Some architects see programming as an element of the design process, whereas others insist it is a separate preliminary step. According to Palmer (1981, p. 10), "Some architects . . . feel that the difference between the natures of programming and designing is too significant for both activities to be performed by the same person. The two tasks are delegated to separate pro-

gramming and designing specialists. On the other hand, some architects see programming as a direct extension of the design process, in spite of the different perspectives of a design problem. They argue that separation of the activities inhibits the necessary continuity between handling the design problem and its solution."

Although programming and designing each require a different style of thinking, the scope of both processes appears to overlap, whether the programmer and designer are the same person or two unrelated professionals. Programming is mostly analytical and systematic, yet it involves the synthesis of information into usable programmatic concepts. Design is intuitive, predicated on synthesis and the creation of form, yet the designer must analyze alternatives and options. Both programming and design are decision-making processes. Programming "enables and produces a progression of increasingly refined decisions involving interaction of [owner], programmer and designer" (Palmer 1981, p. 10).

Although most architects' training provides them with the tools to learn how to design a building type they are not already familiar with, not all architects are proficient at, or interested in, developing a program for such a facility. Many, in fact, prefer to commence their design services only upon receipt of an owner-furnished comprehensive program developed by a planner, space management consultant, or another architect. The more specialized the project, the more important it is to have the program developed by a qualified specialist.

Chapter 5

Estimating Project Costs

The Project Budget

The project budget will likely go through many phases during the life of the project. It should be modified as necessary to reflect changes in the planning, design, and construction processes.

A preliminary budget must be established during feasibility planning and before any design decisions are made. The budget serves as a yardstick by which existing funds can be measured against required capital. It also establishes cost parameters within which both the owner and the architect are willing to work. If either party doubts the appropriateness of these limits, their concerns should be addressed early on.

Of the three variables that coexist within the limits of the budget—cost, scope, and quality—at least one must always be flexible. If costs are fixed and unexpected conditions are encountered, either the scope or the quality of the project must be reduced. The project budget should therefore always include "contingency funds" for unanticipated development and construction costs.

The first step in determining a budget is to identify the project's potential for success by conducting a market survey of the area to be served. The survey looks at persons who are both actually and potentially in need of a service, as well as at existing and potential competitors who can fill that need. A market survey should identify trends in community growth, extent of service areas, and existing and anticipated providers within each service area.

If the market survey suggests a demand for the proposed services, the next step for the planning team is to conduct an economic feasibility study. This study should identify in general terms the amount of money necessary for both development and operation of the facility; at the same time it should project an anticipated yield or return on initial investments. Assumptions must be made at this time regarding building size and net-to-gross area ratios in order to calculate estimated operating and construction costs as well as projected revenues.

Elements of Project Cost

Construction costs are only a part of overall project costs. The cost of land, as well as financing, operational expense, and maintenance expense, must also be considered.

The budget estimate form (figure 10) identifies the major elements of project cost. They are organized into three distinct categories:

1. Direct Construction Costs
   - Building costs. The cost of structural components, walls, floors, partitions, and finishes, along with their associated labor costs.
   - Site development. Site improvement costs, such as grading, excavation, backfill, and the installation of utilities throughout the site.
   - Landscaping. Types and arrangement of foliage, walkways, benches, and so forth.
   - Fixed equipment. Permanent equipment that is not a furnishing or a piece of movable equipment. (The distinction between fixed and movable equipment can be confusing and can lead to misinterpretation of project cost estimates. For example, built-in paging systems are fixed equipment, but desk telephones are movable equipment.)
   - Utilities. Systems and equipment, including electrical, plumbing, heating-ventilating-cooling (HVAC), and fire protection, that are internal to the building or that extend just beyond its external limits.
2. Indirect Construction Costs
   - Site acquisition. The purchase price of land and associated expenses.
   - Contractor's profit and overhead.
   - Furnishings. Furniture, draperies, carpeting, and special finishes.
   - Allowances and contingencies. A predetermined amount, usually a percentage of direct construction costs, set aside for unforeseen conditions, such as undesirable subsurface site characteristics, or for anticipated but fluctuating costs, such as wage rates, that might increase by the time the project is bid.
   - Miscellaneous costs. Artwork, signage, and similar costs.
3. Project Development Costs
   - Professional fees. Architects' and consultants' fees.
   - Site survey.
   - Insurance.
   - Lawyers' and accountants' fees.
   - Postconstruction leasing and advertising.
   - Financing. Interim construction financing, as well as long-term financing expenses.
   - Permit fees. The cost of regulatory reviews, building permits, and so forth.
   - Taxes.
   - Miscellaneous development costs.

When discussing the budget, owners should be clear about whether they are referring to total project costs, total construction costs, or only direct construction costs. Also, it is important to specify which pieces of equipment will be included in project cost estimates and which will be budgeted separately. It is not uncommon for the cost of some specialized medical equipment to exceed the cost of the structure housing it.

Some items, such as furnishings and landscaping, may be controlled by the project team. Others, such as prevailing interest rates, are beyond the control of the project team.

Developing Construction Cost Estimates

Cost estimates become more complex as the project progresses and more information becomes available. "Broadbrush" estimates are adequate at preliminary stages, but later phases should include estimates with enough detail to enable the project team to compare the value of alternative designs.

Construction cost estimates used for feasibility studies are commonly determined by multiplying an appropriate cost factor by the estimated gross building area or volume. During programming, expensive specialty areas can be distinguished from less-expensive general-use areas (for example, an operating room costing $200 per square foot versus a storage area costing $65 per square foot), thus enabling more accurate estimates.

At the completion of each design phase, either a statement of probable construction cost (a cost estimate) should be developed or a previous one revised. The type of estimates prepared during each phase might be as follows.

Schematic Design Phase— Outline Subsystems Estimate

During the schematic design phase (development of conceptual or schematic drawings), alternative layouts need to be compared. Options for major elements of each building subsystem (structure; heating, ventilating, and air conditioning; and so forth) should be briefly examined and tentative selections made. For example, a steel structural frame may be

Figure 10. Budget Estimate Form

Project name _____   Bldg gross square feet _____

Location _____   Net square feet _____

_____   Net/gross ratio _____
Total project cost/
_____   square foot _____
Direct constr cost/
square foot _____

Owner _____

Job number _____   Site area square feet _____

Direct Construction Costs

Building cost (gross area X unit cost/square foot) _____

Site development _____

Landscaping _____

Fixed equipment _____

Utilities

   Heating/ventilating/air conditioning _____

   Plumbing, fire protection _____

   Electrical systems _____

SUBTOTAL _____

Indirect Construction Costs

Site acquisition _____

Contractor's profit and overhead _____

Furnishings _____

Allowances and contingencies _____

Miscellaneous (describe)

_____ _____

_____ _____

_____ _____

SUBTOTAL _____

(continued next page)

A budget estimate form identifies the major elements of project cost.

Figure 10. Budget Estimate Form (continued)

Project Development Costs

Professional fees

  Architectural   _____

  Consultant (_____) _____

  Consultant (_____) _____

  Consultant (_____) _____

Site survey   _____

Insurance   _____

Legal   _____

Accounting   _____

Financing

  Interim   _____

  Long-term   _____

Permit fees   _____

Taxes   _____

Miscellaneous (describe)

  _____

  _____

  _____

                            SUBTOTAL   _____

TOTAL PROJECT COST   _____

Notes:_____

_____

_____

_____

deemed more appropriate than concrete, based on the architect's experience with similar projects. Such decisions will be influenced by regional trends, the availability of materials, applicable building codes, prevailing wage rates, and project scope. A typical outline subsystems estimate includes an estimate for each of the project's major subsystems (figure 11).

Relatively high contingency allowances (10 to 20 percent of the estimated project cost) are appropriate at this stage to compensate for the lack of detailed information available. If estimated construction costs exceed those anticipated in the project budget, the schematic design phase is an appropriate time to suggest changes in project cost, scope, or quality.

Figure 11. Outline Subsystems Estimate

Subsystem	Estimated Cost
Foundation	$_____
Substructure	$_____
Superstructure	$_____
Building enclosure	$_____
Roofing	$_____
Interior construction	$_____
Conveying systems	$_____
Mechanical systems	$_____
Electrical systems	$_____
Equipment	$_____
Sitework	$_____
Allowances and Contingencies	$_____
Total Estimated Construction Cost	$_____

A typical outline subsystems estimate includes the anticipated cost of each of the project's major subsystems.

Design Development Phase— Expanded Subsystems Estimate

As more detailed information becomes available, tentative selections made during the schematic design phase can be tested. An expanded subsystems estimate compares alternative building components and assemblies (for example, precast concrete versus aluminum wall panels) by assigning unit costs per square foot of area or other unit of measure. The outline estimate developed during schematic design can be expanded to enable comparisons of alternative subsystems or entire building systems (figure 12).

The expanded subsystems estimate is detailed enough to provide reasonably accurate predictions, yet design options are still flexible during the design development phase. If estimated construction costs exceed those anticipated in the project budget, this is also an appropriate time to suggest changes in project cost, scope, or quality.

Construction Documents Phase—Unit Rate Estimate

As the final selection of materials and methods of construction is completed, the project team should be aware of the cost ramifications. Previously developed subsystems estimates can now be analyzed in more detail. The unit rate estimate incorporates costs of the individual elements that make up each subsystem. The construction cost of basement walls, for example, may include concrete, formwork, waterproofing, and damp-proofing.

Material quantities multiplied by their respective unit costs yield the total direct costs of construction. Indirect costs, such as contractor's profit and overhead, must also be included to make this figure meaningful. Additional items include cost escalation contingencies and allowances for the requirements specified in the general conditions of the construction contract.

Although a unit cost estimate is useful at this phase to establish a pre-bid estimate, such detailed calculations are generally beyond the scope of the architect's basic services. Cost-estimating consultants often are engaged at this point, and compensation for additional services may be in order, depending on the details of the architect-owner agreement.

Figure 12. Expanded Subsystems Estimate

System or Subsystem	Unit of Measure	Unit Cost	Quantity	Estimated Cost
1. Foundation				
Standard conditions	Linear feet of perimeter	_____	× _____	$_____
Unusual conditions	Linear feet of perimeter	_____	× _____	$_____
2. Substructure				
Slab	Square feet of slab	_____	× _____	$_____
Basement walls	Square feet of wall	_____	× _____	$_____
3. Superstructure				
Floor structure	Square feet of floor	_____	× _____	$_____
Roof structure	Square feet of roof	_____	× _____	$_____
Stairs	Number of flights and stairways	_____	× _____	$_____
4. Building Enclosure				
Exterior walls	Square feet of wall	_____	× _____	$_____
Exterior doors and hardware	Number of leaves	_____	× _____	$_____
Exterior windows	Square feet of windows	_____	× _____	$_____
5. Roofing				
Roofing system	Square feet of roof	_____	× _____	$_____
6. Interior Construction				
Partitions	Square feet of partition	_____	× _____	$_____
Finishes	Square feet of finished area	_____	× _____	$_____
Specialties	Number of items or units	_____	× _____	$_____
7. Conveying Systems				
Elevators	Number of stops, number of elevators	_____	× _____	$_____
Moving stairs	Length or number of flights	_____	× _____	$_____
Pneumatic tubes	Number of stops	_____	× _____	$_____
Hoists	Pounds or tons of carrying capacity	_____	× _____	$_____

(continued next page)

A typical expanded subsystems estimate includes the anticipated cost of each component of the project's major subsystems.

Figure 12. Expanded Subsystems Estimate (continued)

System or Subsystem	Unit of Measure	Unit Cost	Quantity	Estimated Cost
8. Mechanical Systems				
Plumbing	Number of fixtures	_____ × _____		$_____
HVAC	Tons of MBTUs	_____ × _____		$_____
Fire protection	Square feet of protected area	_____ × _____		$_____
Medical gas system	Number of stations served	_____ × _____		$_____
9. Electrical Systems				
Distribution	Kilovolt amps (KVA)	_____ × _____		$_____
Lighting	Square feet of area served	_____ × _____		$_____
Emergency power and lighting	Square feet of area served	_____ × _____		$_____
Fire alarm system	Square feet of area served	_____ × _____		$_____
Nurse call system	Square feet of area served	_____ × _____		$_____
Closed-circuit television	Square feet of area served	_____ × _____		$_____
Telephone system	Square feet of area served	_____ × _____		$_____
Security system	Square feet of area served	_____ × _____		$_____
10. Equipment				
Special equipment (such as laboratory equipment)	Cost per item	Itemize the cost of each unit separately		$_____
Special construction (such as radiation protection)	Square feet of area	_____ × _____		$_____
11. Site work				
Site preparation/ demolition	Square feet of area	_____ × _____		$_____
Site improvements	Square feet of area	_____ × _____		$_____
Site utilities	Length of runs	_____ × _____		$_____
Off-site work	Cost per task	Itemize the cost of each task separately		$_____
12. Allowances and contingencies				$_____
TOTAL ESTIMATED CONSTRUCTION COST				$_____

Chapter **6**

Site Concerns

Site Selection

Once the decision has been made to develop the freestanding facility, a variety of suitable locations must be examined. Site selection can be complicated, and a variety of issues must be considered before arriving at a final decision. A comprehensive examination of these concerns is found in Lifton and Hardy's *Site Selection for Health Care Facilities* (1982).

Because the perfect site may not exist or be available, a few best choices should be identified and compared to one another. In this way, the relative strengths and weaknesses of each can be analyzed and a sensible selection made.

The most important issues in site selection are those relating to location and accessibility, although those affecting the site's development potential also are significant. The following brief discussion of key issues is adapted from Lifton and Hardy (1982).

Proximity to Patients and Other Providers

An old adage says, "The three most important qualities of real estate are location, location, and location." Any service facility should be located near its users. The first step in determining a good location is to project who the potential users of the services are and where they live and work. The proximity of alternate sites to these potential users should then be determined in terms of mileage and time, taking into account existing roadways and traffic problems. It is also important that projections be made based on future as well as existing conditions. A site that is on the outer fringes of a current target area might be in its center in five years if growth trends are in that direction.

The ambulatory care center is required to operate as a successful business. Therefore, it is necessary to map the locations of competing facilities and of those facilities that might aid in its success by referring patients or by providing services that the center lacks. It is necessary to determine what services the center will provide before doing this analysis.

The proximity of competing services can influence the proposed facility's chances of success. This is particularly true in urban areas where distances traveled are typically short. It is possible to map present conditions and current trends, but one can never be certain about what facilities may move into or out of the area in the future.

Studies have shown that patients tend to be more willing to travel in the direction of a population center than away from it, even if the distances are the same. Therefore, direction of travel also can be an important consideration.

It may be helpful to map the entire health care network for the city, state, and region to see how the proposed facility will fit into the existing system. Although providers may be scattered throughout the region, each may have its own special capabilities, such as services found at a trauma center, burn center, or cardiac rehabilitation center. These will likely influence the success of the proposed project.

Major Road Access

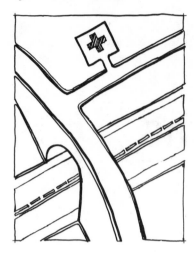

A well-designed building is of little value if it is not easily accessible. Even a building that is well-located within its projected market area must be accessible by private car or ambulance, on foot, or by mass transit. Furthermore, these routes should be convenient for both staff and patients. A slow and indirect route or one with constant traffic congestion is tedious for anyone. Urgent care patients should be afforded a speedy direct route because a delayed arrival could affect their medical condition. For nonurgent patients, a remote or hard-to-reach location may be reason enough to choose another health care facility.

Obviously, rural and urban sites have different acceptable ranges of traffic congestion. Because an inner-city location may be close to its patient population in distance but not in arrival time, calculations of proximity should be made in both miles and minutes. Furthermore, both existing and proposed thoroughfares should be considered. "Generally, the ideal is for a hospital [or health care facility] to be close enough to a major highway that access to the general area of the site is easy from all directions, yet not so close to the

road that noise and congestion result" (Lifton and Hardy 1982, p. 15).

Accessibility by Public Transportation

The importance of access by public transportation is influenced both by the general location of the site (urban versus rural) and by the degree to which public transportation already exists. The more easily individuals can reach the site without assistance or having to drive themselves, the better off the facility will be.

In addition to being a convenience for the patient, public transportation should be considered as an amenity for staff. Both existing and future public transportation routes should be examined, and the possibility of altering these routes can be considered. If the new facility is to have a close association with other health care facilities, such as nursing homes or physicians' offices, an independent shuttle system may be beneficial. Such a system would be particularly useful for connecting a hospital-sponsored satellite facility with the main hospital.

Direct Access

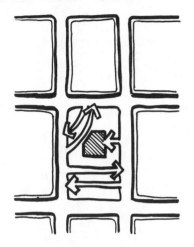

Depending on the nature of the facility, a variety of transportation routes within the site may be required—for example, emergency, nonemergency, patient, service, and staff. All routes should be clearly visible from the street and coordinated so that they do not conflict with one another. It is also important that on-site traffic congestion and peak parking loads be anticipated and provisions made so that they do not complicate off-site circulation.

A site with streets on many sides will likely enable adequate segregation of traffic, making it easy for special routes to be directed to specific areas on the site without interrupting other routes. ''The ideal situation is to have three sides of a site on existing streets or roads, allowing easy access to the site once vehicles have reached the general area'' (Lifton and

Hardy 1982, p. 18). It should be assumed that many users of the facility are already under stress and do not need the further aggravation of having to decipher a cryptic transportation network.

The type and size of roadways bordering the site must be examined carefully. Single lanes and one-way streets may cause unnecessary congestion, whereas auxiliary roads adjacent to the site may alleviate tie-ups on the major roads during heavy use.

Size and Usable Area

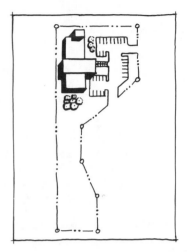

The actual size of a site is not necessarily an accurate indicator of the amount of area that is usable. In determining the amount of usable land needed, building configuration, parking, and circulation patterns should all be considered. In addition, local building and zoning codes must be researched, as they often require building setbacks and may further restrict the usable area, including parking and circulation layouts.

Consideration should also be given to the need for expansion, as the site might be of adequate size for present needs but not for future growth. ''A contingency allowance of 30 percent [for expansion] has been suggested by some authorities, although no data have been collected on whether or not this is an appropriate allowance. Some provision for the future, regardless of whether or not it is arbitrary, is important'' (Lifton and Hardy 1982, p. 14). Figure 13 illustrates a site containing an existing building. Three alternative development options are shown.

Figure 13. Site Analysis

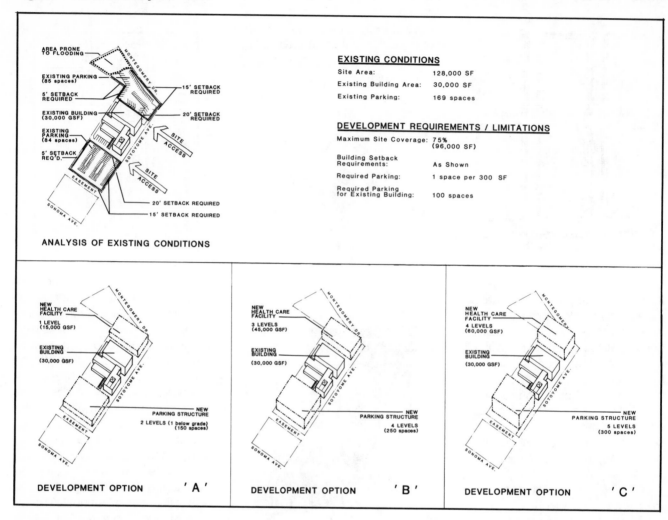

Figure 13 identifies the development requirements of an existing site and illustrates three alternate development options for meeting those requirements.

Configuration and Orientation

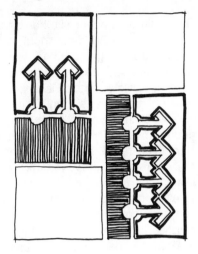

In addition to size, the geometry and configuration of a land parcel can determine its relative usable area. For example, a long and narrow parcel might not have the depth required to lay out buildings, parking, and circulation efficiently, whereas a smaller but more regular parcel would. The site configuration should accommodate the greatest amount of design freedom—building configuration, location within the site, and circulation and parking arrangements. Although square or slightly rectangular geometries are most likely to allow such freedom of design, other configurations can be considered. Sites with gross irregularities or unusual topography, however, may present unnecessary design constraints.

The following questions pertaining to site geometry should be asked:

- What is the geometry relative to the street frontage?
- Does it allow for easy access and egress?
- Does it allow for separate public and service access?
- Does it allow for separate emergency and nonemergency circulation?

- Does it allow for individual parking clusters along the periphery, or only one central parking lot?
- Can convenient circulation routes be arranged around and through the site without unnecessarily compromising the building depth and/or configuration?

Site orientation refers to the placement of a building in relationship to surrounding features. Lifton and Hardy (1982) suggest the following questions for consideration:

- How does the site relate to nearby physical features, such as hills?
- For sites that are not square, does the site have its long axis along a road so that site access is suitable?
- Is the site oriented so that the structure can take advantage of natural features, such as the sun, for efficient heating and cooling of the building?
- Can a building erected on the site be seen easily from nearby streets and roads?

Each of these factors is not likely to be of great importance individually, but combined could have some impact on the overall suitability of a [health care facility] site (Lifton and Hardy 1982, p. 16).

Zoning

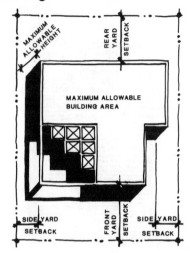

Most municipalities have zoning requirements based on land use. Local codes should be reviewed to see if any restrictions exist. If any do, it is sometimes possible to have land rezoned, or to obtain a "conditional use permit," through an often lengthy and costly process.

Some zoning ordinances specify required setbacks and restrict the size, height, and type of building. Most codes specify required parking areas and loading zones, often on the basis of a building's occupancy classification. Before any schematic designs are initiated, a thorough investigation and interpretation of applicable codes must be completed.

The existing zoning of adjacent sites should also be examined by the owner. Will the neighbors be compatible in terms of noise, character, appearance, and traffic, or will they detract? Will they be likely to refer patients, or will they serve as competition?

Easements and Restrictions

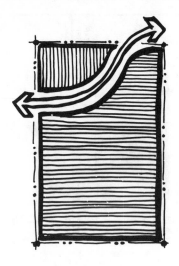

Once the site has been evaluated in terms of configuration and orientation, it must be examined more closely to see if easements or restrictions will adversely affect its development potential. Although it is common for a site to have some restrictions, the exact nature and location of each restriction will determine the effect it has. For example, a utility easement prohibiting any construction within its limits may be easily worked around if it runs along a minor property line. A similar easement running through the property, however, may virtually split the site in two and seriously hinder economical development.

Legal restrictions may be in the form of easements, covenants, trust agreements, or previous subdivision rules. They may restrict location of construction on the site, type of use, or the size or height of a building. "Identification of easements can be done by contacting the relevant utilities, reviewing a site survey, if one exists, and/or examining the existing title to the property" (Lifton and Hardy 1982, p. 18). This is the time to enlist the help of architectural, engineering, and legal consultants.

If the facility anticipates using emergency transportation by air, regulations affecting landing patterns should be investigated.

Restrictions also may be the result of physical conditions. Hills, swamps, and rivers are easily detected, but flood plains, inadequate bearing soil, and contaminated ground water are less obvious. These conditions all require further professional investigation.

Legal and physical restrictions that limit a site's development potential should be assigned priorities and separated into those that can be worked around and those that cannot. The cost of such adjustments must then be added to the cost of the site. A careful analysis should be done to identify seemingly peripheral influences on the site—both positive and negative. These include views, vegetation, noises (from nearby factories or overhead airline routes), odors (from factories or sewage plants), and the general appearance and reputation of the area. In most cases, detracting influences can be architecturally screened out and amenities can be added.

Environmental Impact

Regardless of whether an environmental impact statement is required by the government, the degree to which the new facility affects the existing community and landscape should be addressed. Both the building itself and the related structures—roads, pathways, sewage disposal, and traffic—should be considered. If the facility is to be considered a beneficial element by the community, its appearance should also be of concern to the planning team. (Facility image is discussed in chapter 10.)

Site Utilization

By the time an actual site has been selected, a good deal should be known about it, including visual characteristics, nearby influences such as traffic and noise levels, and existing natural and manufactured features such as vegetation, buildings, and roadways. This knowledge may be derived from field inspections, land and regulatory surveys, and soil borings.

Although the purpose of site selection is to acquire a site that optimally satisfies program requirements, not all of those needs will be evident at that preliminary stage. To ensure a proper "fit" between building and site (figure 14), the following questions should be considered:

- Along what part of the site's perimeter will curb cuts be located to provide access and egress between the building and the street?
- To what extent is future growth anticipated? What parts of the site, if any, will accommodate facility expansion?
- How many parking spaces will be required? Will parking be on-site, along adjacent streets, or in existing parking facilities? Will covered parking be provided?
- Will staff and public circulation be mixed or separated? Will more than one drop-off zone be provided?

Some of these requirements can be determined by analyzing operational data. Work load projections, for example, will yield the optimal number of parking spaces to be provided (see chapter 8, Analysis). Although zoning codes may dictate the minimum number of spaces required for a specific building type

Figure 14. Site Utilization

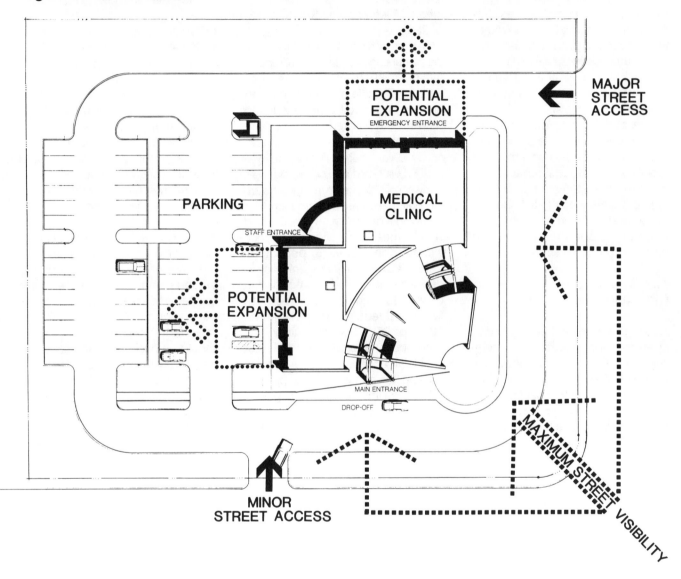

Figure 14 depicts a small medical clinic situated to accommodate future expansion and to maximize street visibility. (Reprinted with the permission of Kaplan/McLaughlin/Diaz Architects and Planners, ©1986.)

and size, they do not necessarily provide optimal parking facilities. Site requirements should be analyzed by testing various programmatic concepts such as separate versus mixed circulation and centralized versus decentralized parking areas (see chapter 9, Synthesis).

Site and building issues cannot be widely separated. Design for both internal and external concerns must proceed somewhat simultaneously, with the development of each moving from the general to the specific. In this way, site development can respond to changes in building design and vice versa.

Circulation

Access to the site has been discussed as an important criterion for property selection. Once the property has been selected, a system for circulation through the site must be developed. The following methods of transportation for staff, patients, and supplies should be considered:

- Private automobiles
- Emergency vehicles (in some instances, helicopters)
- Supply and delivery vehicles
- Walking
- Wheelchairs
- Mass transit

The volume and frequency of each of the above will be a factor of both location and services to be offered. A rural site probably will have fewer pedestrians than will an urban one. Primary care patients are more likely to travel by scheduled public transportation than urgent care patients, who will typically arrive by taxi, private car, ambulance, or on foot. It is desirable "to separate, insofar as possible, the various kinds of traffic—pedestrian from vehicular and patient,

staff, visitor, and service from each other" (Allen and von Karolyi 1976, p. 226).

In many cases, a patient undergoing ambulatory surgery will be dropped off and picked up by a friend or relative. Therefore, patient parking areas and drop-off zones should be conveniently located near appropriate entrances and exits.

Vehicular routes should be well marked with bold and simple signage. They should proceed from their starting points with as few turns, curves, and points of conflict as possible and should meet the building entrance without compromising pedestrian traffic. If an emergency entrance is desired, "it should be positioned downstream and as far as possible from signalized intersections" (Kanaan 1973, p. 67). This will minimize the likelihood of interference with other vehicular access routes. Adequate parking for nonemergency patients will reduce their temptation to park in emergency areas.

It should not be overlooked that some patients may have no alternative but to arrive on foot, especially in an urban setting. Both pedestrian and vehicular access should be direct, easy to follow, and free of conflicts from the edges of the site to the entrance of the facility. Routes will be easier to follow if users can orient themselves; that is, if they can see their destination from a distance (see chapter 8, Analysis).

Barrier-Free Access

All buildings should be accessible by handicapped persons. For obvious reasons, the freestanding ambulatory care facility should be particularly responsive to this concern. Too often designers equate handicapped access only with designing for people in wheelchairs. The disabled popula-

tion, however, includes persons with:

- Partial or total loss of mobility
- Partial or total loss of vision
- Partial or total loss of hearing
- Mental disabilities

Of those with partial mobility losses, many are ambulatory with activity limitations. Some limitations are due to the effects of heart and lung diseases or arthritis and rheumatism. Mechanical aids used by these persons include canes, walkers, braces, artificial limbs, and special shoes. Although the impairments of these persons are not always as obvious as those of wheelchair-bound persons, their total numbers are greater and their need for special design considerations is just as important. "Pedestrian walkways should be designed with occasional off-the-path rest areas, [minimal slope,] and nonslip surfaces that are stable, firm, and relatively smooth. Adequate lighting and proper maintenance are also important" (American Society of Landscape Architects 1975, p. 13).

Plans for Growth

Once established, site circulation routes have the effect of physical features on the landscape in the sense that they may restrict future facility expansion. Phasing plans should therefore be established at the onset of design to ensure proper coordination of internal and external developments. Site amenities such as walkways, landscaping, and parking areas should be coordinated with internal circulation networks and should also be adaptable to future expansion. (Planning for future growth is discussed in more detail in chapter 9, Synthesis.)

Parking

Adequate parking accommodations are important not only to encourage patients to use the facility but also to attract qualified physicians and staff. In calculating parking requirements, the following questions should be answered:

- What categories of persons are expected to use the facility? For example, visiting physicians, staff, patients (emergency, primary care, and so forth), and visitors.
- How many from each group are expected to need parking spaces? For example, 60 percent of staff, 100 percent of emergency patients, and 100 percent of all visiting physicians.
- What is the expected duration of the parking needs for each category of person? For example, staff: full day or one full shift; emergency patient: one hour; and so forth (Allen and von Karolyi 1976, p. 232).

If the facility is to be open for more than one work shift, shift overlaps during a peak load should be used to determine parking demand. Some geographic locations see drastic seasonal variations in patient loads, which should also be taken into account. Additional parking space should be provided to accommodate overflow and to prevent bottlenecks during unusually busy periods.

Parking assignments must be recognized for their political implications. Covered, reserved parking for select staff members is analogous to the business executive's solid walnut desk as an indication of status.

Walking distances from parking lots should be kept as short as possible, and locations of lots should be coordinated with the interior circulation of the building.

It seems self-evident but is sometimes forgotten that patients [who come] to clinics and emergency rooms are often old and infirm, that they may require assistance in walking, and that parking spaces for these people should be as close as possible to the entrance they must use. Obstetric patients should also be provided drive-up and parking space close to the entrance.... Physicians should be assured space by designating a specific area and perhaps restricting its use by a card-operated gate. With these exceptions, where a special need exists for immediate access, the use of parking space will be most effective when consolidated to the maximum (Allen and von Karolyi 1976, p. 235).

Drop-Off Zones

The need for special drop-off arrangements for such services as urgent care, ambulatory surgery, and physical therapy should not be overlooked. The following items should be considered:

- The drop-off zone should be a minimum width of 12 feet to allow the car doors to be fully opened for ease of access.
- Length of the zone should accommodate at least 2 cars, allowing 25 feet for each, and should have gradual access to the main road.
- Where the zone is at the same grade as the adjacent walk, bollards (posts) or some other suitable device should be used to separate the two areas. Where a curb exists and cannot be removed, a [gradual ramp] should be provided to make the grade change.

- Signage should be provided to identify the drop-off zone and limit its defined use to a "pick-up and drop-off" function (American Society of Landscape Architects 1975, p. 38).

Each locale may have its own applicable codes and standards, which should be reviewed carefully as they may override the general guidelines given above.

Chapter 7

Organizational Concerns

To understand the functional organization of any facility, one must first become familiar with a basic vocabulary of its parts. The following terms apply to any building type. Familiarity with them allows us to perceive and categorize the overall organization of a building or group of buildings.

Building Size

The overall construction cost of a building can be directly related to its size. However, because many items are required regardless of the building's size and because cost per square foot of area generally decreases when large areas are involved, the overall unit cost of the building likely will decrease as building area increases.

How, then, does one determine the optimal size of a proposed facility? Space programming is not a magical trick. Rather, it is the logical transformation of anticipated facility utilization statistics into functional area requirements. The goal of planning is to maximize the potential for revenue-generating activities while minimizing the cost of supporting those activities. A building that is too small cannot adequately perform needed services; one that is too large costs more to build and operate than it generates in revenue. Understanding a building's revenue-generating potential relative to its overall size can be achieved by analyzing its floor plan in terms of space types, efficiency ratios, and user zones.

Space Types

Most facilities are composed of three types of space: *activity, support,* and *administration* (figure 15). *Activity space* refers to spaces used directly for the primary activity or purpose of the facility. An activity space in a surgical facility would be an operating room. Other activity spaces might include examination, treatment, and special procedure rooms.

Support space includes those spaces that directly assist the function of an activity space. Patient lockers and waiting areas are support spaces. So are bathrooms, telephone and vending booths, storage rooms,

Figure 15. Space Types

ACTIVITY
  Surgical Procedures
  Exam / Treatment
  Special Procedures

SUPPORT
  Clean / Soiled Utility
  Nurses' Station
  Lockers / Toilets

ADMINISTRATION
  Reception
  Offices
  Clerical / Filing

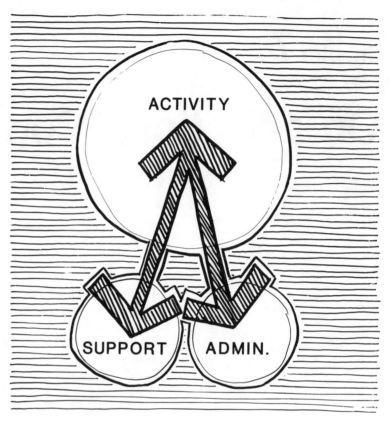

Any building can be divided into activity, support, and administration spaces. The area required for support and administration space is determined by the type and quantity of activity space programmed.

utility rooms, janitor closets, and laboratory spaces. A laboratory might be considered support space if it exists only to serve some other activity, such as surgery. However, if laboratory procedures are a primary activity of the facility, the laboratory might be considered activity space.

Administration space houses staff members when they are not engaged in the primary activity of the facility. These spaces include offices, conference rooms, and clerical areas.

Key Space Generators

The amount of space required to accommodate a given activity is determined by first identifying that activity's *key space generators*. A key space generator is a quantifiable estimate of patient, staffing, or equipment loads. It is expressed in terms of quantity (3 operating tables), frequency (3,000 surgical procedures per year), and duration (1.5 hours per procedure).

The amount of activity space needed is then determined as a function of the key space generators (each operating room can accommodate X procedures per day and takes up Y square feet of space). The owner of a facility often can provide accurate estimated work load data, but the services of an architectural or planning consultant usually are needed to transform these data into

meaningful area requirements. (See chapter 8 for further discussion of key space generators.)

Support and administration space is allocated on the basis of the programmed activity space, which is determined by the projected work load. The amount of revenue the facility is able to generate is influenced by the proportion of activity space to support and administration space. Figure 16 shows how activity space and support space are allocated, relative to the size of the facility.

Assignable Areas

Space type should not be confused with *building area.* The former identifies the functional zones of the facility and is used to determine how they are organized. It identifies qualitative relationships. The latter, which identifies building size, can be used to estimate the project cost and plan efficiency. Building area calculations,

identifying quantitative relationships, can be expressed in terms of either *net* or *gross* area. Net area can, in turn, be expressed as either *assignable* or *unassignable* area.

Net assignable area is composed of all the functional spaces required

to serve the basic program.

Net unassignable area consists of all other spaces in the building, specifically circulation areas, mechanical areas, general toilets, janitor closets, unassigned storage, walls and partitions.

Figure 16. Relative Proportion of Space Types

Activity Space
Support Space
Administrative Space

Figure 16 illustrates the relative proportions of activity, support, and administration space in this ambulatory surgery facility. (Reprinted with the permission of Kaplan/McLaughlin/Diaz Architects and Planners, ©1986.)

Gross area is defined as the sum of both net assignable and unassignable areas (Peña 1977, p. 101).

The efficiency ratio (net assignable area ÷ gross area) represents the relative efficiency of the floor plan. It is usually expressed as a percentage.

The higher the number, the more efficient the plan (figure 17). By rearranging the equation, net assignable area requirements can be used to project the gross building area (Peña 1977, p. 108).

User Zones

Most buildings can be divided into *user zones.* A zone may be identified by its activity type (a surgical zone) or by a boundary that it implies (public, staff, and mixed zones). The

Figure 17. Efficiency Ratio

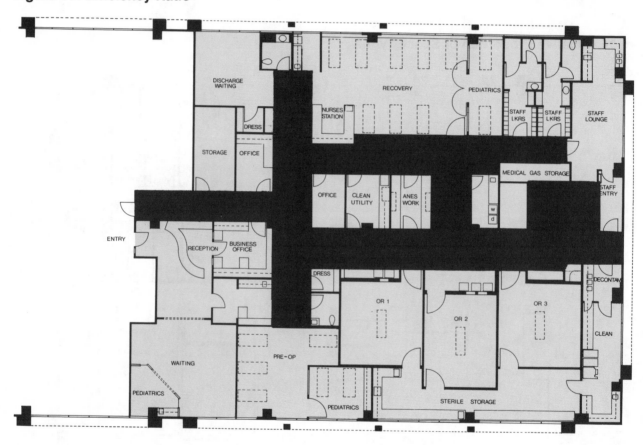

Net Assignable Area: 5945 SF
Gross Building Area: 8038 SF
Efficiency: 74%

☐ Assignable Area
■ Unassignable Area

Net assignable area divided by gross building area equals building efficiency. The higher the number (which is often expressed as a percentage), the more efficient the plan. (Reprinted with the permission of Kaplan/McLaughlin/Diaz Architects and Planners, ©1986.)

latter form of classification is useful for determining building-to-site relationship requirements, such as entry, parking, and delivery. It also can identify where control must be provided, typically at the transitional boundaries between both public and staff zones.

Control devices may be required to restrict the flow of patients, to limit sound transmission, or to block views (figure 18).

Figure 18. User Zones

■ Public Zone
□ Staff Zone
□ Mixed Zone

Figure 18 demonstrates internal zoning as determined by public, staff, and mixed-use areas. (Reprinted with the permission of Kaplan/McLaughlin/Diaz Architects and Planners, ©1986.)

Circulation Patterns

Circulation patterns through a building tell a great deal about its functional efficiency. A simple, concise circulation system usually indicates a well-organized plan, whereas one with many confusing intersections indicates a less successful arrangement. In general, the simpler the circulation, the more effective it will be. The three subsystems that make up the circulation system of a health care facility are *patient flow, staff flow,* and *equipment flow* (figures 19 and 20).

Patient Flow

Patient flow begins miles away from the facility. Although the architect has little control over the territory beyond the property line, the building form and configuration affect its visibility from a distance. Both the street

Figure 19. Flow Diagram

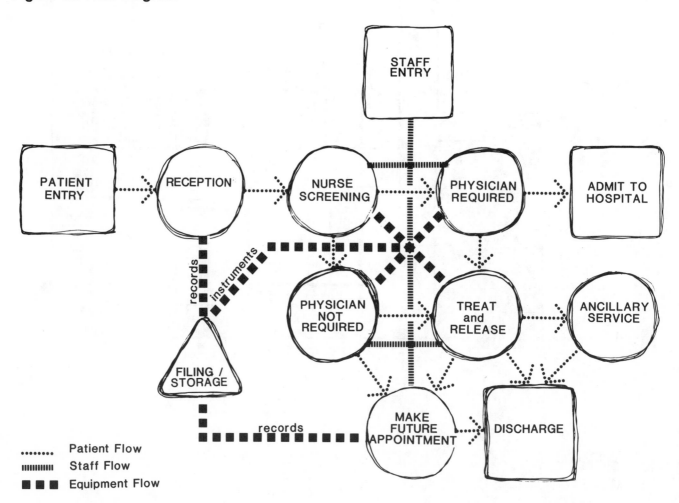

The circulation system of a health care facility is made up of patient flow, staff flow, and equipment flow. (Adapted from *The Health Maintenance Organization Facility Development Handbook,* U.S. Department of Health, Education, and Welfare, 1975.)

entrance and the building entrance should be recognizable well in advance of arriving at the property. If multiple entrances exist, they should be differentiated, especially if one is for emergency access. Entrances can be articulated by their form, size, shape, color, or material. Parking entrances should be easy to find and parking areas should be situated for easy building access.

An initial contact point (receptionist, triage station, information desk) should be clearly visible from the point at which a patient first enters the building. A person immediately confronted with many paths to choose from is likely to get lost. The circula-

Figure 20. Circulation Patterns

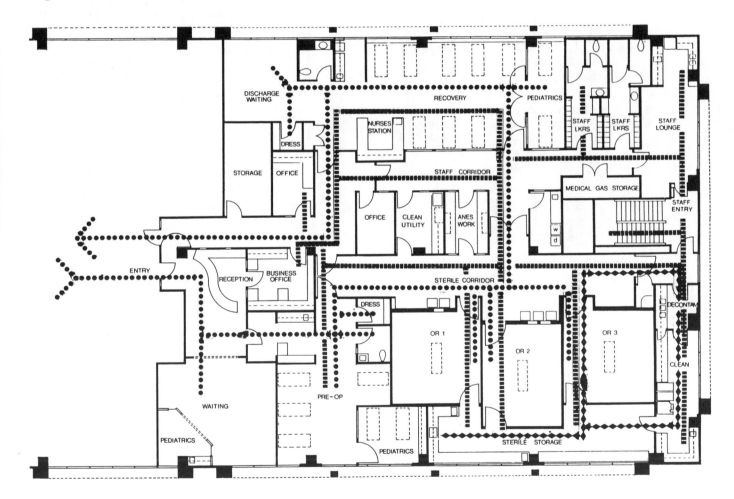

- •••• Patient Flow
- ▪▪▪▪▪ Staff Flow
- ◆◆◆◆ Equipment Flow

Circulation conflicts can easily be avoided by mapping out circulation patterns. (Reprinted with the permission of Kaplan/McLaughlin/Diaz Architects and Planners, ©1986.)

tion system should be self-evident; signage should supplement, not provide, the visual cues. Although paths are often thought of as planar, they are actually three-dimensional and can be articulated volumetrically, perhaps defined by colonnades or skylights.

Staff Flow

Site-related staff flow is easier to accommodate than site-related patient flow, primarily because the staff is familiar with the facility. Internal staff flow is often separated from patient flow. A separate staff entrance allows physicians to enter and exit without passing through public zones. Frequently traveled routes should be kept short whenever possible. A 10-foot path that is traveled every five minutes soon becomes a long trail. The appropriate arrangement of functionally related spaces can alleviate the problems of cumbersome staff circulation.

Equipment Flow

The complexity of an equipment flow system is a function of both the complexity of the facility and the degree to which each function requires movable equipment. Equipment flow can be divided into three categories: the transport of machinery, the delivery and return of medications and supplies, and the movement of trash. Each is concerned with storage, cleanliness (sterility and the control of infection), and scheduling.

The building's circulation system is integrally related to its system of planned growth and expansion. The planning of circulation within the health care facility, which is by nature predisposed to change and renovation, must incorporate relevant growth planning criteria.

Part III

Applying Planning Principles to Freestanding Facilities

Chapter **8**

Analysis

The fundamental planning issues described in part II can now be applied specifically to a freestanding ambulatory care facility. This two-step process consists of analysis (collecting and analyzing relevant data) and synthesis (formulating concepts that will influence the organization and layout of the facility). Synthesis is discussed in chapter 9.

Data Collection

After project goals have been established, facts must be collected and analyzed in order to develop useful planning tools. Such data collection often begins with interviews between the architect and the owner. One tool used to document work load statistics is a data collection form. It is worded in such a way that the owner can provide data in the form of operational expectations—for example, the number of anticipated patient visits per day. The questions are primarily concerned with work load, staffing patterns, growth expectations, average length of procedures, percent of facility downtime, and interdepend-

ence among different services. This information is necessary for determining the overall scope and size of the facility as well as for understanding the facility's unique characteristics.

Figure 21 is a data collection form filled out for a hypothetical ambulatory surgery center. This form typically is filled out by the architect or programmer during interviews with the owner and staff and may be modified as necessary.

Data Analysis

Key Space Generators

Work load statistics from data collection forms serve as *key space generators* in determining the number of required primary activity areas (see chapter 7). For example, an anticipated annual work load of 4,200 procedures (work load statistic) might imply a need for three operating rooms (primary activity areas) in an ambulatory surgery center. These three rooms might, in turn, require an additional 3,000 net square feet

Figure 21. Data Collection Form

Department or service _Outpatient Surgery_   Date _July 1986_

Facility name _Ambulatory Surgical Center_

Location _San Francisco, California_

Owner _O. P. Surgeon, M.D._

Occupancy classification _B-2 (UBC-82)_   Construction type _II-B (UBC-82)_

1. Type of Facility   ☒ Freestanding   ☐ Attached to hospital

                Activity areas: Support areas:

                   ☐ Attached to hospital   ☐ Attached to hospital

                   ☒ Separate from hospital   ☒ Separate from hospital

Description: _Freestanding outpatient Surgery Facility. Owned and operated by independent physician group. Preferred Provider arrangement with hospital "X" in San Francisco._

2. Projected Work Load Indicators

Type of Procedure	No. of Procedures/Year	Avg. Duration (Incl. clean-up)
Minor Orthopedic	1,200	1.35 hrs.
Gynecological	1,200	.60 hrs.
Ophthalmological	1,000	.60 hrs.
Cosmetic	800	1.21 hrs.
Total procedures/year	4,200	
Avg. duration/procedure		.94 hrs.

3. Projected Hours of Operation

Operational hours per day _9_   Procedure hours per day _6_

Open _7 AM_   Close _4 PM_   Days open per week _5_

                                       ☒ Mon   ☒ Tue   ☒ Wed   ☒ Thu   ☒ Fri   ☐ Sat   ☐ Sun

Operational days per year _250_

Number of work shifts per day _1_

(continued next page)

This form documents information necessary for developing a facility space program. The data include anticipated work load statistics, facility organization and usage patterns, and a description of any requirements that might influence space programming.

Figure 21. Data Collection Form (Continued)

4. Projected Staffing

Staff Position	FTEs per Shift (Avg)
M.D.	3.5
R.N.	3.
L.P.N. (L.V.N.)	3
Anesthesiologist	2
Aide	1
Clerk	2
Receptionist	1
Technician	2
Other: _Anesthetist_	1
Other: _____	_____
Other: _____	_____
Total FTEs *per shift*	18.5

5. Activity Spaces or Workstations

Name of Area	Special Requirements
Operating Room	
Recovery (Adult)	Controlled natural Lighting Preferred
Recovery (Pediatric)	" " "
Pre-Operative Holding	

6. Supply System

☐ Exchange cart system   ☒ Circulating bulk cart

☐ Other (describe) _____

_____

_____

(continued next page)

Figure 21. Data Collection Form (continued)

7. Instrument Processing within Facility

☒ Flash sterilization   ☒ Decontamination

☒ Sterile storage   ☐ Wrap/prep

☐ Other (describe) _____

_____

_____

8. Required Functional Relationships

Describe: _Good visibility between nurse station and recovery & pre-op areas._
Provide infection control at all entry points to sterile corridor from non-sterile
zones.

Illustrate:

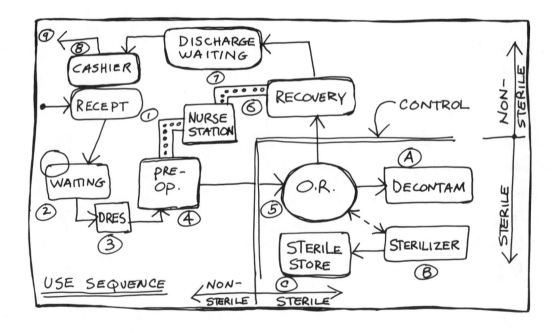

of support and administrative space. Figure 22 shows the calculations required to arrive at the optimal number of operating rooms for a facility, based on information from the data collection form (see figure 21).

Key space generators should be identified for each independent primary activity area. These units of measure may be in the form of the number of annual or daily visits, pieces of specific equipment, or number of personnel who will be occupying the space. The number of beds may also be a unit of measure for ambulatory facilities that are functionally related to a hospital's inpatient services.

Any given primary activity area may have more than one type of key space generator. Furthermore, the way in which services are provided may influence which key space generators are most useful for determining area requirements. This concept

Figure 22. Example of Calculations to Determine Space Needs

The number of required operating rooms is derived from the following basic formula:

Projected annual procedures ÷ projected annual procedures per operating room = projected number of operating rooms needed

It is assumed that the projected annual procedures per operating room is a function of the average procedure duration, including set-up and clean-up time, and the number of hours per day for which the operating rooms are used (see figure 21).

Using the example in figure 21, the average procedure duration is 0.94 hours. Although the facility is open 9 hours per day, the operating rooms are used during only 6 of those hours, to allow time for patient recovery before discharge. Down time for clean-up is also accounted for in these figures. The facility operates 250 days of the year. On the basis of these figures, the average number of potential procedures per day per operating room is calculated as follows:

6 hours/day ÷ 0.94 hours/procedure = 6.38 procedures/day/operating room

Even allowing for down time and recovery and clean-up, scheduling will not be 100 percent efficient. In this example, an 85 percent efficiency factor is used to account for time in which an operating room is available but not used. Therefore, the projected number of annual procedures per operating room in this example is as follows:

6.38 procedures/day X .85 efficiency factor X 250 days/year = 1,355 procedures/year/operating room

Referring back to the original formula,

4,200 projected annual procedures ÷ 1,355 projected annual procedures/operating room = 3.10 operating rooms

Therefore, the architect or programmer should allow for 3 operating rooms.

Figure 22 describes the process of determining the number of activity spaces needed to accommodate the key space generators identified in the data collection form (figure 21). In this example, the activity spaces are operating rooms and the key space generators are projected annual procedures, hours of operation, and average procedure durations.

can be illustrated by comparing two clinical laboratories, both having the same annual work load, one processing its samples manually and the other using a fully automated system. The size of the first laboratory is determined primarily by the number of personnel needed to perform testing procedures. The size of the second, however, is determined by the space required to house the automated processing equipment.

The 'key space generator' approach addresses all potential space seekers in the final functional and space program. Workload-related or 'primary activity' space is determined from workload volumes trans-lated into workstations. A workstation is the basic activity space required to perform a given task: it may be a room, such as an office or procedure room, or it may be one of several activity spaces in the same room, such as a counter or a desk. Operating rooms and examination rooms are exam-

Figure 23. Functional Room Space List

Ambulatory Surgery Center	
Primary activity areas, net square feet (NSF)	2,500
Administrative areas (NSF)	412
Support areas (NSF)	1,984
Functional area summary (NSF)	4,896
NSF-to-DGSF multiplier	1.50
Dept gross square feet (DGSF)	7,344
Dept-gross-to-bldg-gross multiplier	1.10
Bldg gross square feet (BGSF)	8,078

Area Name	Description	No. of Areas	Net Sq Ft
1. Primary Activity Areas			
General operating room	360 NSF minimum, 400 NSF desired	3	1,200
Pre-op, adult	3 beds, 80 NSF per bed	1	240
Pre-op, pediatric	2 beds, 80 NSF per bed	1	160
Recovery, adult	8 beds, 80 NSF per bed	1	640
Recovery, pediatric	2 beds, 80 NSF per bed	1	160
Examination room		1	100
Total			2,500
2. Administrative Areas			
Office, supervisor		1	112
Office, anesthesiologist		1	64
Office, business/clerical	3 persons	1	156
Office, interview/consult		1	80
Total			412

This list identifies all the assignable rooms within a facility and net areas are given for each room. Net area multiplied by various multipliers (see appendix A for a discussion of multipliers) yields departmental gross area and building gross area.

ples of spaces that are planned on the basis of workload volumes. (Hayward et al. 1985, p. 9)

Space Inventory

After the data collection form has been completed, a detailed space inventory can be compiled. It is often helpful to assemble both a written room-by-room functional space list (figure 23) and a graphic space inventory (figure 24). The written list is useful for noting functional room requirements, such as a nurses' station with direct visual connection to postoperative recovery areas, and for identifying applicable code requirements, such as the minimum allowable net square feet per bed or gurney in preoperative and recovery rooms. Later, the list can be expanded to catalog special equipment required for each room.

The graphic diagram adds proportion and scale to the functional room space list. For instance, when eight gurneys are superimposed

Figure 23. Functional Room Space List (continued)

Area Name	Description	No. of Areas	Net Sq Ft
3. Support Areas			
Decontamination		1	72
Instrument processing		1	160
Sterile core/supply		1	200
Dressing area, patient	20 NSF	2	40
Nurse station/charting	Direct visual communication to recovery and pre-op areas.	1	100
Work room		1	108
Scrub station	18 NSF, 2 sinks per station	3	54
Utility room, clean		1	80
Utility room, soiled		1	80
Storage, miscellaneous		1	60
Storage, clean equipment		1	60
Storage, gurney	21 NSF	2	42
Housekeeping closet		1	18
Locker room, women	12 persons	1	50
Locker room, men	15 persons	1	80
Toilet/shower, women		1	100
Toilet/shower, men		1	100
Staff lounge		1	120
Toilet, patient		1	48
Toilet, pre-op		1	48
Waiting area, adult	10-12 adults	1	180
Waiting area, pediatric		1	64
Discharge waiting		1	120
Total			1,984

Figure 24. Graphic Space Inventory

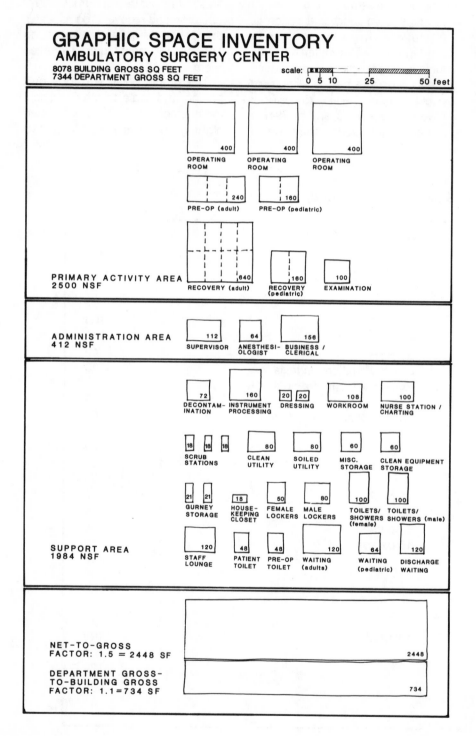

A graphic space inventory visually communicates the information described in the functional room space list (figure 23). When drawn to scale, it allows the planning team to visually comprehend the size of the facility as well as the relative proportion of one area to another.

within the outline of a 640-net-square-foot recovery room, minimal room dimensions become apparent, as do implied circulation paths. Graphic space diagrams can be simple, showing only area requirements (figure 25), or detailed, showing furniture, special equipment, and critical dimensions (figure 26).

When the latter approach is taken, the diagram should be viewed only as a generic layout, rather than as a final design solution. When programming complex buildings or those with complicated services, detailed room diagrams are useful for highlighting critical space requirements such as the optimal distance between recovery beds to accommodate emergency lifesaving equipment and personnel. For simpler programs, or when the planning team is familiar with the intricacies of the facility, a simple single-line graphic room inventory will suffice.

During the initial stages of the inventory, space requirements are usually expressed in terms of net square footage, thus enabling project team members to check the accuracy of their estimates. By dividing each element into activity, support, and administration spaces, one can visualize service area efficiencies. If gross square-foot estimates are needed, the total net area assigned to each service can be multiplied by an appropriate net-to-gross factor, which will vary from function to function but will likely be within the range of 1.1 to 1.6. To determine the total building area required, an additional multiplier must be factored in to account for stairwells, elevators, exterior walls, and corridors not previously included. (See appendix A, Space Programming Methods, for more information on selecting appropriate multipliers.)

Figure 25. Simple Graphic Space Diagram

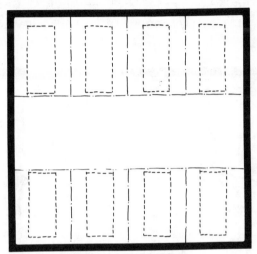

Recovery Room—640 NSF

Often a simple outline describing a room's net area provides adequate programmatic information to the designer. The advantage of simple diagrams is that they encourage the designer to explore architectural alternatives without suggesting one "best" solution.

Figure 26. Detailed Graphic Space Diagram

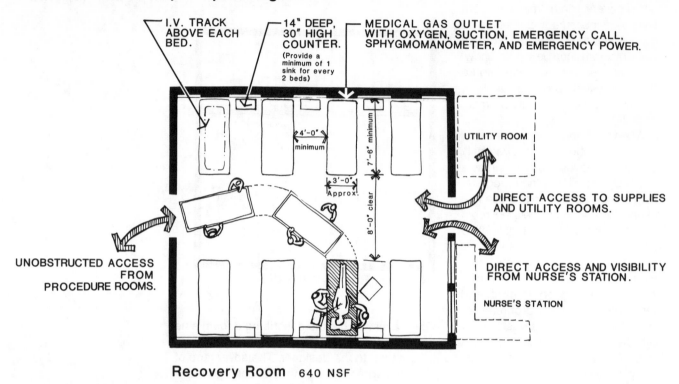

Recovery Room 640 NSF

Sometimes the programmatic requirements of a room are so detailed that they need to be visually communicated to the designer. This diagram of a surgical recovery room shows recommended gurney spacing, visual and circulation requirements, and equipment locations. A recovery room of equal size but different configuration could be functionally unacceptable.

Work Sessions

Periodically, the entire project team should get together to verify data that have been assembled up to that time. Well-organized information and skillful team leadership are essential to productive work sessions. This is the time to distinguish between personal wishes and project goals and to separate proven facts from persuasive opinions.

Rare is the project that does not require major changes throughout the planning process. It is important that team members allow such changes to be made without losing continuity of either the process or the project.

Chapter 9

Synthesis

After data on projected work loads, staffing requirements, and space requirements have been condensed and organized into a workable format, the project team should once again clarify its goals to ensure that appropriate methods of attaining them will be used. These methods, which we will refer to as "concepts," will later influence design decisions. The formation of concepts is the first step in synthesizing the previously analyzed data.

The following 12 concepts, considered relevant to almost any project, are described in *Problem Seeking: An Architectural Programming Primer* (Peña 1977, pp. 62-75). These concepts are discussed in the balance of this chapter to illustrate various ways in which the freestanding ambulatory care facility can be organized.

- Service grouping
- People grouping
- Activity grouping
- Spatial relationships
- Priorities
- Security controls

- Flexibility
- Sequential flow
- Separated flow
- Mixed flow
- Orientation
- Energy conservation

Service Grouping

Elements of the service system include building maintenance, environmental controls, power and utilities, and the process of circulating medical and nonmedical supplies and equipment. Concepts may be considered that call for centralization of some elements and decentralization of others (figure 27). A building that houses both limited-use and continuous-use (24 hours a day) facilities might suggest a decentralized heating, ventilating, and cooling system to serve only those spaces in use, and at the same time suggest a single centralized loading dock to simplify delivery procedures.

Figure 27. Service Grouping

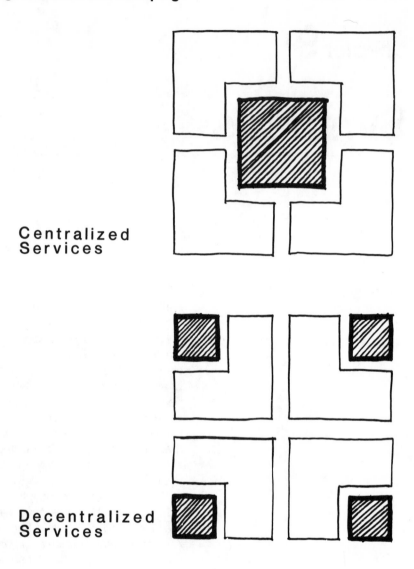

Centralized
Services

Decentralized
Services

People Grouping

One of the marketable attributes of the freestanding facility is its intimate scale, which some patients prefer to the clinical atmosphere of large hospitals. This quality should be considered when determining the character of spaces in which people will congregate (figure 28). Some activities require intimacy or privacy (chemotherapy is an example); others, such as some aspects of physical therapy, may be enhanced by group interaction.

A human-scale environment may encourage intimacy and interaction. One's perception of scale, however, is affected by more than just size and proportion. Noise transmission, views, and color all can be used to heighten one's feelings of either security or insecurity. A window in a waiting room disclosing a small but pleasant garden can provide comfort for disoriented persons. Similarly, separate small waiting areas might be considered in order to allow for intimate and private grouping of people.

Figure 28. People Grouping

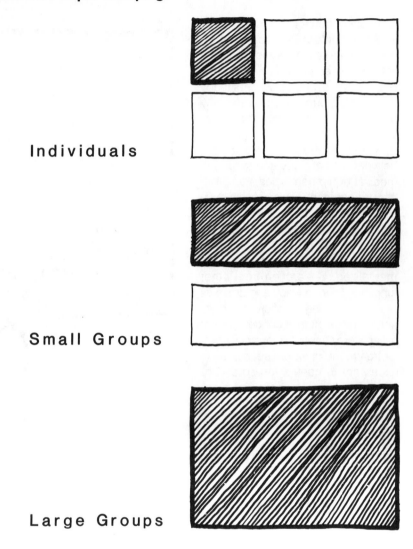

Individuals

Small Groups

Large Groups

Activity Grouping

The concept of activity grouping differentiates integrated spaces from compartmentalized spaces. Some activities are enhanced by close proximity to others. Such closeness tends to promote group interaction and may provide an opportunity for cross-utilization of staff.

Figure 29 shows a clinic located between a pharmacy and a durable medical equipment sales area. With this arrangement, clinic patients have easy access to retail areas, and all three activities can share the services of a small support staff.

Some activities are best compartmentalized. Separation from other functions offers privacy and prevents unwanted mixing of different populations. This is often a concern where patients are sensitive about their need for treatment, or where separation is necessary to control the spread of infection and to prevent contamination of sterile supplies.

Figure 29. Activity Grouping

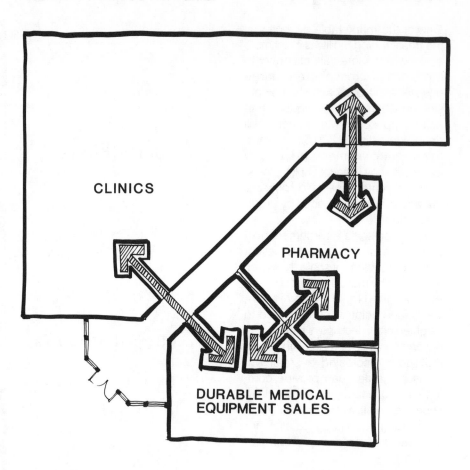

Spatial Relationships

Spatial proximities signify a desired or necessary functional linkage between two or more areas. Conversely, spatial barriers signify a functional separation between areas. Linkages and barriers between spaces must be thought of both qualitatively and quantitatively, with concern for urgency, convenience, and frequency. Figure 30 illustrates the spatial relationships of an ambulatory surgery center.

Interdepartmental spatial relationships in a hospital differ from those in a freestanding setting. Consider the

relationship between the surgery and emergency departments of a hospital and that between ambulatory surgery and urgent care in a freestanding outpatient center. In the hospital setting, the two departments have a strong linkage based on the frequency and urgency of patients being transported from the emergency room to the operating room. As a result, the two departments are generally found in proximity.

However, the nature of the services rendered at an ambulatory surgery center and an urgent care center differ considerably from those of in-hospital surgery and emergency

departments; therefore, their respective spatial relationships also differ. As discussed in chapter 2, urgent care rarely implies trauma, and ambulatory surgery is intended for scheduled low-risk procedures. Thus, the urgent and frequent transportation link from urgent care to ambulatory surgery is nonexistent.

Consider this linkage in reverse: If ambulatory surgery patients require emergency stabilization, the urgent care facility, by definition, is probably not the place to take them. As a result, the two areas do not require the functional proximity implied by their names. A wise arrangement, however,

Figure 30. Spatial Relationships

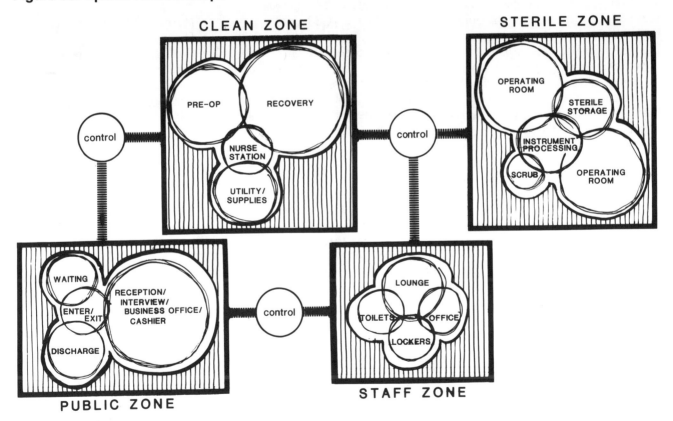

Figure 30 illustrates the relationship of spaces within a surgical suite. Space clusters separated from other spaces are known as zones. Control points (doors, windows, work stations, and so forth) regulate the flow of noise, light, vision, and objects from one zone to another.

would be to locate both services near accessible emergency lifesaving equipment.

Means of transport must also be considered when determining spatial relationships. Family practice services, for example, depend on rapid access to patients' medical records. This access may be accommodated either by physical proximity or by an efficient system for extracting and transporting records before the patient arrives. Automated systems with remote storage and access capabilities also provide an alternative to physical adjacency.

Priorities

The concept of priority gives rank and relative importance to goals and to the variety of means by which goals are accomplished. For example, a priority of minimizing expenses might result in stark, sterile-looking hallways. On the other hand, a priority of providing user comfort and convenience might result in tastefully appointed hallways, inasmuch as connecting corridors are areas frequently seen by the patient. Given the present climate of aggressive marketing of health care services, it is appropriate that traditional priorities be continuously reevaluated.

When budgets are inflexible, as they usually are, it is easy to see how one high-ranking priority may cause others to be lost or forgotten. Project goals must, therefore, be clearly understood by everyone involved in the planning process. It is necessary for the project team to identify the relative importance of priority elements early on if conflicts are to be resolved during subsequent design phases.

Security Controls

Security controls are implemented to protect the well-being of both property and people. "The degree of security control varies depending on the value of the potential loss— minimum, medium, or maximum" (Peña 1977, p. 69).

The usual security system is designed to protect against burglary or theft; however, access control to sensitive areas is another valid application. For example, the operating suite during surgery must be protected from infection by unsterilized personnel or equipment. Similarly, contagious...patients ...must be isolated from unauthorized personnel and visitors (Garrett 1973, p. 38).

Concepts of security control, activity grouping, people grouping, and flow (sequential, separated, or mixed) are all closely related. It is easy to see how mixed grouping of patients in a waiting area can cause both annoyance and the spread of germs. Separate children's waiting sections are often created for this reason. Mixed-use facilities, in which some activities are continuous while others are limited in duration, pose additional challenges to providing security. A well-zoned building in which certain areas are temporarily shut down can be advantageous in such a situation.

Security controls consider necessary egress while preventing unwanted ingress. Evacuation systems must respond to fire, smoke, explosions, noxious gases, or the sudden loss of power. Elements of the system should include warning devices, such as alarms, as well as countermeasures, such as automatic sprinklers.

An evacuation system will be of little value if exits are not clearly marked and if the circulation system is complicated or confusing. Depending on its size, the building may need to be partitioned into small areas with fireproof doors and walls. Local and/or national codes specify such requirements, which are generally a function of building size, construction type, occupancy classification, zoning requirements, and the particular fire zone.

Although building codes vary by region, some guidelines are applicable to most situations. The following items, identified by Malkin (*The Design of Medical and Dental Facilities,* 1982, p. 293) as pertinent to planning medical office facilities, apply equally well to the planning of other freestanding health care facilities.

- Minimum width of corridors
- Number of exits
- Bathrooms to accommodate the handicapped
- Separation of exits
- Maximum length of dead-end corridors
- Construction of partitions
- Fire separations
- Radiation shielding
- Fire detection devices or sprinklers

Flexibility

The building environment should be regarded as a living organism in the sense that it, too, is capable of growth and adaptability. For example, the facility may be projected to grow in distinct phases. The architectural solution must accommodate this while allowing for a variety of unplanned changes that are likely to occur. Figure 31 shows the floor plan of a large medical office building designed for flexibility.

In designing for flexibility, the plan-

Figure 31. Medical Office Building Designed for Flexibility

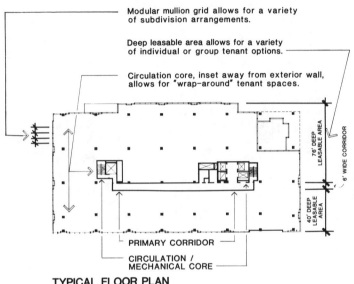

Modular mullion grid allows for a variety of subdivision arrangements.

Deep leasable area allows for a variety of individual or group tenant options.

Circulation core, inset away from exterior wall, allows for "wrap-around" tenant spaces.

PRIMARY CORRIDOR
CIRCULATION / MECHANICAL CORE

TYPICAL FLOOR PLAN WITHOUT TENANT IMPROVEMENTS

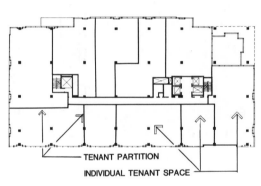

TENANT PARTITION
INDIVIDUAL TENANT SPACE

TYPICAL FLOOR PLAN SHOWING A VARIETY OF INDIVIDUAL TENANT SPACES

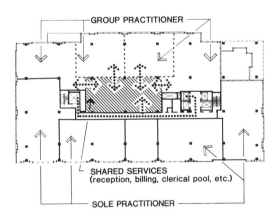

GROUP PRACTITIONER

SHARED SERVICES
(reception, billing, clerical pool, etc.)

SOLE PRACTITIONER

FLOOR PLAN SHOWING GROUP PRACTICE WITH SHARED SUPPORT SERVICES

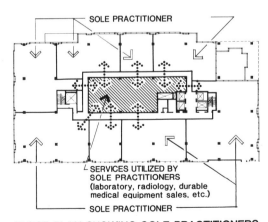

SOLE PRACTITIONER

SERVICES UTILIZED BY SOLE PRACTITIONERS
(laboratory, radiology, durable medical equipment sales, etc.)

SOLE PRACTITIONER

FLOOR PLAN SHOWING SOLE PRACTITIONERS UTILIZING INDEPENDENT SUPPORT SERVICES

Pacific Presbyterian Professional Building was planned using the "mega-floor-plan concept," in which one leasable area was made deeper than normal to accommodate a variety of possible tenant arrangements. (Reprinted with the permission of Kaplan/McLaughlin/Diaz Architects and Planners, ©1986.)

ning team should first identify which areas are of a fixed nature and which are flexible. Large equipment stations with utility hookup requirements do not lend themselves to frequent relocation unless they are specifically designed to be mobile (for example, mobile magnetic resonance imaging units). Office space, however, is flexible and can be designed to accommodate future expansion. Toilet and shower areas are moderately "fixed," as plumbing is expensive to relocate. Functions that can readily be relocated are said to occupy "soft" space; those that cannot are said to occupy "hard" space.

The planning team should strive to minimize the disruption of services during all phases of construction. This means that some temporary facilities will likely be required for an interim period, during which all building and safety codes apply to both temporary and permanent areas (figure 32).

Planning for flexibility implies expansibility, convertibility, and versatility.

Figure 32. Phased Expansion

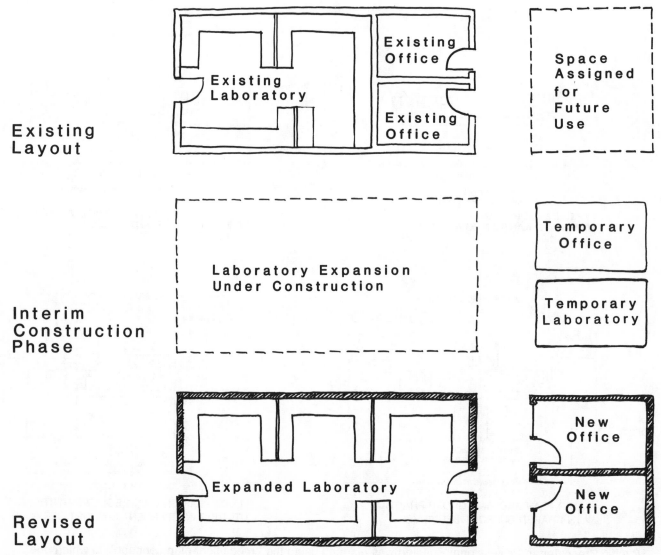

Phased expansion requires a strategy for temporarily relocating all necessary functions until proposed construction is complete.

Expansibility

Expansibility refers to two distinct forms of growth: accretion and cellular growth (figure 33).

Accretion implies that a space "swells" or engulfs more area. An exercise area, for example, can be expanded to allow the use of more equipment.

Cellular growth implies an ideal unit size or increment of growth. If a group practice wants to increase the size of its staff, the facility must expand by adding a set of rooms that will correspond to the increased work load requirements. For example, two examination rooms, one consultation room, and 60 additional net square feet of patient waiting area might be added for each additional staff physician.

Figure 33. Expansibility

Accretion

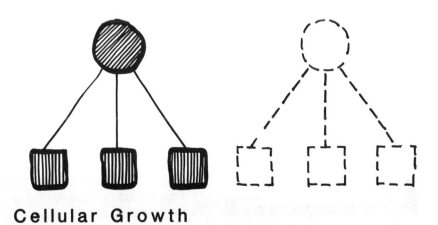

Cellular Growth

Convertibility

Convertibility is the ability of a space to accommodate change in its form and function (figure 34). Once again, the fixed and flexible elements must be identified. Heating and cooling systems can be arranged to accommodate a variety of floor plans.

Similarly, modular wall systems are designed to facilitate convertibility. "There are movable furniture and wall partitions which are part of a system, i.e., modular seamless plastic containers, frames, carts, panels, and rails. All space is considered capable of housing any activity when specialized equipment is moved in to create a tailor-made environment" (Pütsep 1979, pp. 144-45).

Versatility

Versatility is the sharing of multifunctional spaces to accommodate a variety of activities, either simultaneously or sequentially (figure 35).

Some activities, such as physical therapy and fitness, require similar equipment and are easily combined. With proper scheduling, temporal barriers can be used to replace physical ones. Project team members should refer to original project goals to ensure that their decisions are appropriate.

Figure 34. Convertibility

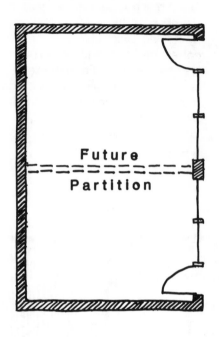

Figure 35. Versatility

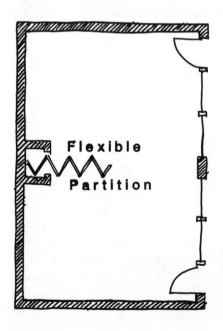

Flow

Flow describes the movement of people and things. Sequential flow indicates progression, separated flow segregates with the use of control points or barriers, and mixed flow promotes planned or chance encounters.

To understand the circulation requirements of each service area, the project team should develop flow systems strategies. One useful tool is the flow chart or diagram (figure 36), which illustrates type and quantity of patient, staff, and equipment flow. Flow charts may be assembled for staff and equipment flow as well as for patient flow (see figures 19 and 20).

In addition to being a descriptive device that is essential to record the way patients flow through a system, the flow diagram is a problem-solving tool in its own right. By diagramming a system and listing priorities for decisions for all paths that patients follow from the time they enter to the time they leave, the analysis often reveals inconsistencies and contradictions within a facility. (Rising 1977, p. 27)

Sequential Flow

Methodologies to improve flow systems include the notion of "queuing concepts...a body of knowledge that systemizes the study of how services are provided sequentially for customers who wait in line" (Rising 1977, p. 5).

A highway tollbooth is a classic example of a queuing system in which the service is the collection of tolls and the arriving customers are the cars approaching the tollbooth. Rising illustrates this concept's application to medical facilities through a series of flow diagrams (figure 37).

Figure 36. Average Daily Patient Flow Chart

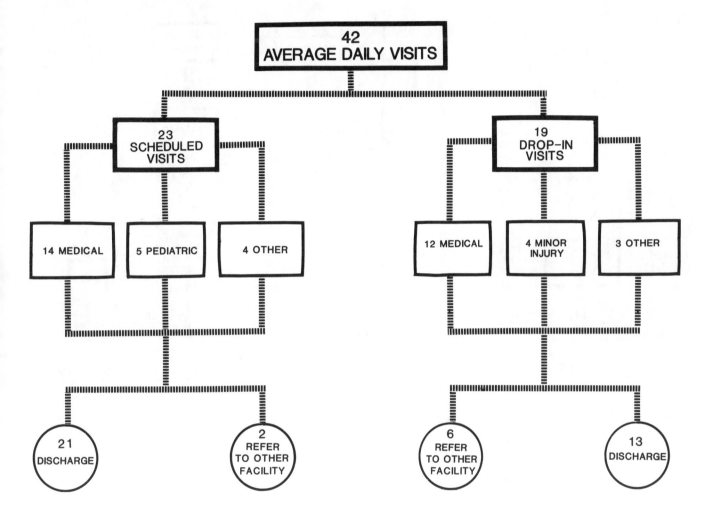

A patient flow chart illustrates types and quantities of patients passing through a system, in this case a primary care clinic.

Sequential flow and spatial relationships are virtually inseparable; in fact, the two can be superimposed to verify one against the other. Flow patterns that backtrack and criss-cross frequently may indicate improper spatial arrangements. A third interrelated factor is the size and number of rooms. A waiting room that is too small will cause discomfort and bottlenecking; one that is too large will be inefficient. The accuracy of the initial operational data—projected patient loads, and so forth—will thus determine the accuracy of the architectural program—number, size, and arrangement of rooms.

Separate Flow

In some areas of the health care facility, a system for the separate flow of staff, patients, and objects is helpful. The separation of patient and staff entries affords convenience and privacy to physicians who might otherwise have to enter and exit through public waiting areas.

Figure 37. Examples of Queuing Systems

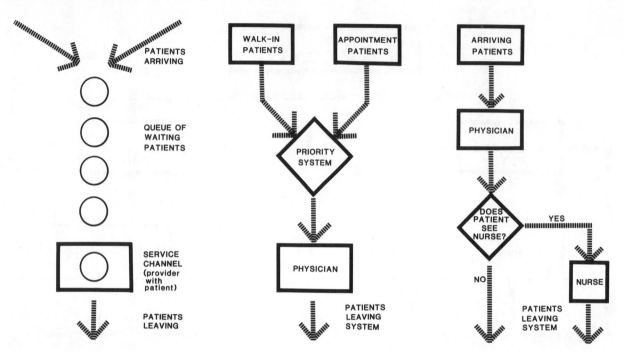

Diagram of a single-channel queue, interpreted as a medical facility.

Example of a single-channel queuing system with two streams of arrivals.

Example of a single-channel queuing system in which some patients go through a single stage and some patients go through two stages in tandem.

Queuing systems describe "the art of waiting in line." Each system suggests a different amount and arrangement of spaces. (Adapted, with permission, from *Ambulatory Care Systems,* vol. I, by Rising. ©1977 by D.C. Heath and Company.)

Segregated flow is commonly implemented in the emergency or urgent care facility. Controls are used to protect patients' privacy and to give order to what can become chaotic circulation patterns. Barriers can block both sound and sight and are frequently flexible rather than permanent.

The concept of separated flow is a basis for spatial arrangements in many medical facilities.

There are three principal spaces: the public space, the medical space, and a control-administrative space separating the other two....We believe that this basic concept of planning should rarely be violated. In order to preserve the privacy and integrity of the medical space, it is imperative that there be a positive barrier (control point), so that no one is allowed into the medical area until the doctor or nurse is ready to begin the examination. (Fleming 1973, p. 46)

Mixed Flow

In contrast to a system of distinct and regulated circulation, mixed flow is often planned when random individual or group interactions are desired. This is often the case in public cafeterias, resource centers, lobbies, and sometimes in waiting areas. Mixed flow is best provided by arranging furniture, plants, walls, and other elements in such a way that territorial boundaries are implied but not rigidly defined. Attention should be given to color, lighting, scale, and selection of materials and finishes. Paths may be loosely defined by a cadence or rhythmic repetition of elements such as columns or posts.

Orientation

By definition, ambulatory patients are persons who can move about from place to place; the freestanding facility, by its nature, is designed to accommodate patients' mobility. Consequently, a prime reason that one chooses a freestanding facility over a hospital is that the former is more easily accessible.

Orientation, or the process of becoming familiar with one's environment, is part of accessibility. The more familiar patients are with where they are going and how they are to get there, the less stressful their visits will be. This is particularly true with patients who feel that their need for treatment is urgent. Cryptic labyrinthian hallways have no place in the ambulatory health care facility. Every effort should be made to minimize patients' disorientation and apprehensiveness.

Every trip begins with a starting point and ends with a destination. Even if a route is not visible from the starting point, it will be easy to follow if the destination is visible. This is particularly important in modularly designed buildings in which one area looks like the next.

Color or material coding of major routes and different floor levels may be helpful for some patients, but not for those who are blind or color-blind or who simply have poor vision. Simple yet distinct geometrical elements are often more recognizable than applied color or guiding stripes. Sometimes a distinct landmark such as a tower or a fountain, visible from within the building, will help the patient to become oriented. Illumination systems such as skylights or strip lights can also be integrated to guide patients along a route (figure 38).

Energy Conservation

Energy conservation is generally concerned with climate, the building site (see chapter 6, Site Concerns), and the building envelope. A successful design responds to all three without compromising operational or aesthetic programmatic requirements.

Climate

Four factors affecting climate are wind, sun, humidity, and temperature. The project team should have relevant climatic data documented and should identify those regional conditions that will affect the building design. Monthly and annual variations should be known for rainfall, snowfall, humidity, temperature, prevailing winds, sun's path, vertical sun angles, and potential natural hazards [such as] hurricanes, tornadoes, earthquakes, etc. (White 1983, p. 20)

Both average and peak highs and lows should be known. Climatic data can often be obtained from the local weather service and can be presented in the form of a graph.

Building Site

Three factors affecting the site are topography, vegetation, and building orientation. A site survey will identify the first two. The latter will be affected by both of these as well as the documented climatic conditions. For example, in a desert climate with high temperatures and occasional seasonal flash flooding, a building might be located in the shade of existing trees and uphill of flood-prone drainages. Furthermore, the building

might be oriented to minimize harsh solar exposure and to maximize the cooling effect of prevailing breezes.

Building Envelope

A goal in energy conservation is to minimize the flow of heat between indoor and outdoor spaces. Sources of heat gain are external solar gain and internal gain from people and equipment. The building envelope (walls, floors, windows, doors, roof) is the surface that separates the indoor spaces from the outdoors. The various materials that make up the building envelope have different thermal properties, as do the various methods of fastening them.

The building envelope should resist heat transfer through conduction, convection, and radiation. This resistance will be determined by the envelope's mass, color, geometry, surface area, and permeability (resistance to infiltration).

Figure 38. Orientation

Circulation route articulated by a row of skylights.

Chapter **10**

Summary and Conclusions

Architectural Concerns

Following is a brief summary of architectural concerns for owners, architects, and planners of freestanding facilities.

Visibility

The building should be easily recognized from both major and minor approaches. Visibility can be emphasized by creative use of color, form, and materials. Entrance identification is essential, particularly if more than one major entrance exists. Ideally, the appropriate entry point should be visible as the patient approaches the site.

Accessibility

The building site should be conveniently located, preferably near major transportation routes but not in an overly congested area. An adequate number of parking spaces, not merely the minimum amount required by local codes, should be provided. Effective site and building circulation

should be direct and completely accessible by physically impaired individuals. Concise signage should supplement the circulation network, rather than provide the sole means of orientation and direction. Convenience and security must not be compromised when some services remain available for extended hours. When access is difficult or confusing, patients will look elsewhere for their health care needs.

Image

Although the building's visibility alone may not attract new patients, its architectural form and image convey a feeling that patients associate with the quality of services within. Image-conscious design implies that a building's presence carries with it a positive message. Although imagery is a highly subjective perception, some universal attributes such as superior quality and accessibility are always appropriate to convey.

An image of superior quality need not imply high expense. Attention to detail signifies high quality and is easily accomplished using standard, inexpensive materials. Careful detailing should be recognized as an integral part of the architectural process rather than something to be resolved on-site during construction. This attitude also applies to the importance of landscaping and other site amenities.

To create an image of accessibility, make the facility easy to get to and easy to get around in. This effect can be enhanced by the architect's sensitivity to scale and proportion and is particularly important in public spaces such as waiting areas and main entries.

Perhaps the best way to develop an "image strategy" is to think of the building as a package containing a marketable commodity, not just as an envelope keeping out the wind and rain. "Packaging" objectives can then be determined in accordance with a previously developed marketing strategy. Affordability or state-of-the-art technology will be more or less appropriate as imagery depending on the targeted market. Similarly, local style and regional patterns can be contrasted or incorporated depending on the message desired. However, resist the temptation to "stick on" image-evoking motifs without regard for overall composition, as this tends to dilute the message.

Flexibility

In an era of rapid technological development and increasingly competitive marketing, facility needs are likely to change many times during the life of a building. Therefore, circulation and layout should accommodate both growth and shrinkage as necessary. Such changes must be planned to afford minimal disruption of simultaneously occurring activities. Chapter 9, Synthesis, discusses various methods of designing for flexibility.

Figure 39 shows a hospital-based freestanding medical office building that is accessible, visible, and flexible; at the same time, it conveys a bold professional image (see figure 31 for the floor plan).

Economy

Above all, the facility must be economically feasible to construct and affordable to maintain. Building efficiency, or the ratio of net usable area to gross building area, is a key determinant of economic success. An efficient layout minimizes unnecessary circulation space and uses double-loaded corridors where dedicated circulation space is needed. Pertinent operational data should be collected early in order to determine quantity, size, and configuration of activity spaces. Procedure rooms that are too small will become functionally obsolete if they cannot be accessed by required equipment and personnel. Similarly, a shortage of storage space will result in dangerously overcrowded corridors or the use of expensive activity areas as closets.

In some states, nonhospital outpatient centers are allowed by code to provide smaller procedure rooms than similarly functioning hospital-based outpatient departments (operating rooms, for example). Minimally sized rooms, however, may create more functional restrictions than construction cost savings.

Efficient design is not measured only by construction costs. Because labor costs constitute such a large percentage of overall health care fees, building layout should facilitate streamlined staffing patterns. This can be accomplished by minimizing "nursing steps," carefully zoning public and staff areas, and by developing floor plans that accommodate

cross-trained personnel. A properly designed facility will reduce operational costs as well as attract qualified professional staff. Furthermore, technological developments that reduce the size and increase the utility of medical equipment, as discussed earlier in this chapter, are likely to reduce many functional space requirements.

Future Forecasts

A hundred years ago, the number of acute care hospitals in this country grew from fewer than 200 to more than 5,000 within 30 years. Today many of our acute care beds lie vacant.

Traditionally, hospitals have represented a centralized "bundle" of medical services, a system in which highly technical equipment and procedures have typically been provided only in specialized tertiary care centers. Although tertiary care facilities still house many of our medical pioneers, the delivery of health care services, by and large, is becoming decentralized or "unbundled." The issues discussed previously in this book give evidence that this pattern will continue.

Within the next two decades, the number and variety of alternative settings for health care services will continue to grow as existing hospitals search for innovative approaches for converting underutilized space. Specific facility types, such as urgicenters or outpatient catheterization laboratories, may come and go in popularity as markets become saturated or as new and economical procedures are developed, but freestanding facilities in general will continue to be economically advantageous.

"Medical malls" or health care

Figure 39. Pacific Presbyterian Professional Building

(Reprinted with the permission of Kaplan/McLaughlin/Diaz Architects and Planners, ©1986. Photo by Douglas Symes.)

shopping centers will increase in popularity as convenience and accessibility continue to influence consumers' decisions. Extended care and skilled nursing facilities will prosper by accommodating the needs of a growing population of the elderly. Similarly, the sale and rental of durable medical goods such as wheelchairs, portable oxygen devices, and portable monitors will continue to occur alongside the sale of such services as sports medicine, home health care, and cardiac rehabilitation. Clusters of networked services will prove more profitable than those of isolated practitioners. This trend may broaden the definition of the term *freestanding,* but growth will clearly continue in the direction of unbundled services.

Communications advances will reduce the need for functionally related services to be adjacent or even near one another. "Instant communication and the transmission of medical data between these facilities will probably be the most profound change from the health care system of the eighties to that of the twenty-first century" (Panther 1985, p. 27).

Digital instrumentation and archiving systems will require smaller record storage areas and increase both the speed of, and allowable distances for, transmitting patient data. The installation of a simple telephone jack will enable any office to access a magnitude of data, view x-ray films stored elsewhere, or monitor the physical progress of a patient at home.

The need to maintain high-quality service under severe economic pressure is perhaps the greatest challenge that faces both health care providers and architects/planners with whom they work. Their ability to provide affordable services without sacrificing quality of care will determine whether we win or lose the health care revolution.

Part IV

Planning Data

Appendix A

Space Programming Methods

Source: Adapted from *The Health Maintenance Organization Facility Development Handbook.* DHEW publication #HSA 75-13025, 1975.

Figure 1. Comparison of Space Programming Methods

Input   Computation   Result

1. Building Rule-of-Thumb

Building Gross

Building rule-of-thumb

2. Net to Gross

Dept. listing
Room types
Room quantity
Room sizes

Net Space Program

Building net-to-gross multiplier

Building Gross

3. Net to Departmental Gross to Building Gross

Method 2   (used as double check)

Dept. listing
Room types
Room quantity
Room sizes

Net Space Program

Department Gross Program

Building Gross

Department net-to-gross multipliers

Department-gross-to-building-gross multipliers

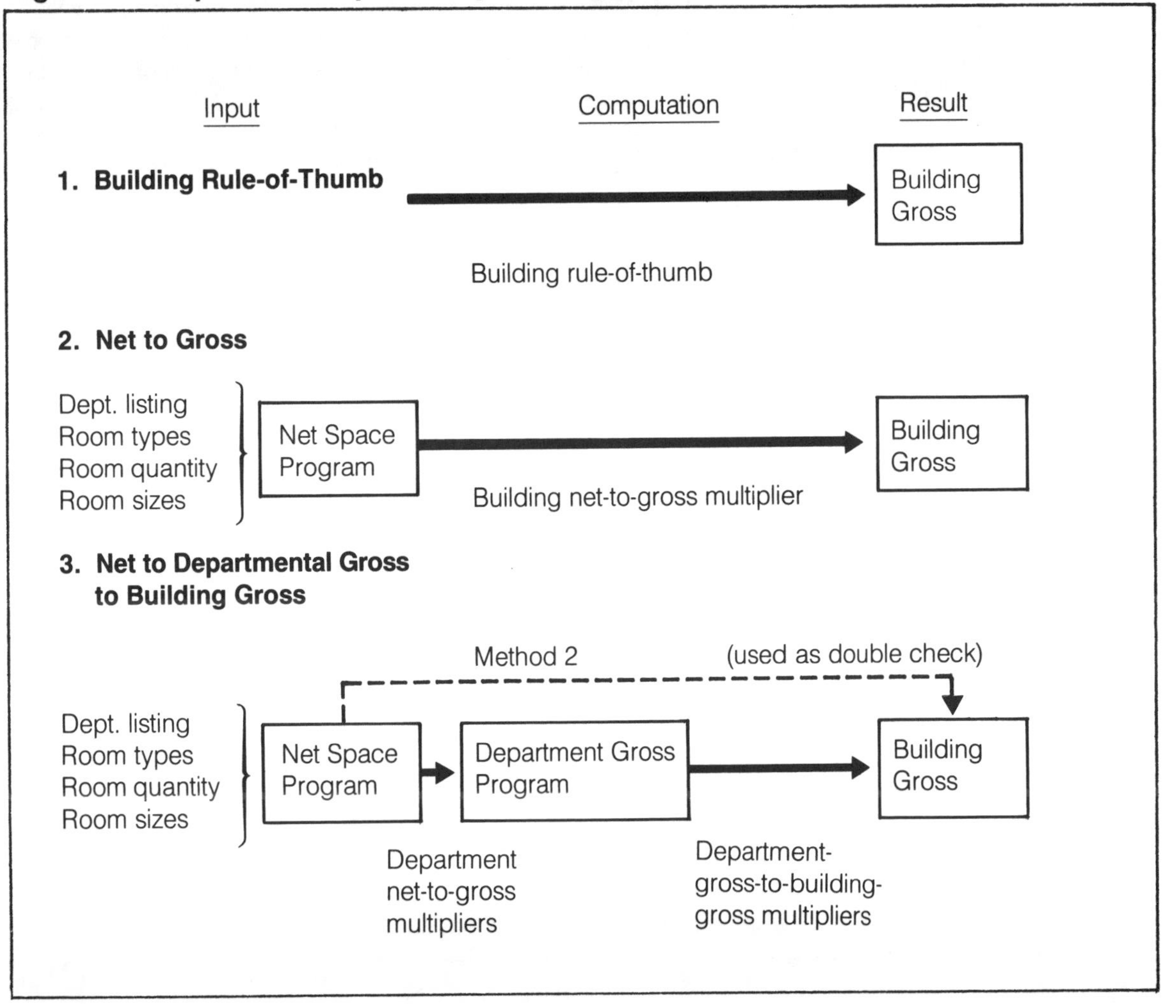

Objectives of Space Programming

The *inputs* for space programming are as follows:

- The functional program
- Knowledge of the size and shape of rooms in which specific medical practices take place
- Knowledge of net space, gross space, and net-to-gross ratios in similar facilities
- Knowledge of the capacity of physical spaces to process medical activity as a function of time

The *outputs* of space programming include the following:

- A complete list of every anticipated, usable room for the project
- The area, in square feet, of each room, as well as recommended minimum dimensions for each room

- Anticipated net-space-to-departmental-gross multipliers and the area of each department
- The anticipated net-space-to-building-gross multiplier and the estimated total building gross area

The method used to convert the input into a space program will depend on the specificity of the desired output, the experience of the programmer, the validity of comparative data, and the programming method.

There are three common methods diagrammatically compared and presented here, in order of increasing complexity, with the necessary backup data to accomplish each objective for an HMO. Naturally, each succeeding level requires more input, but each also implies greater reliability. The three methods are (1) building-type rule-of-thumb method, (2) simple net-space-to-gross-space method, and (3) net space/departmental space/building gross method.

Building-Type Rule-of-Thumb Method

A simple guideline that relates gross area of the building to some aspect of its function can often be established for a particular type of facility. In the HMO, there are three reasonable relationships that can be considered at this simplistic level: (1) square feet per member, (2) square feet per physician, and (3) square feet per patient visit.

The values in table 1, Building Rule-of-Thumb Area Examples, were extracted from careful measurements of 12 HMO or group practice facilities. Each table shows a high-square-foot and a low-square-foot ratio. Note that there is no presentation of an average, or mean; this is to protect against a common programming error, projecting on the basis of unlike facilities.

Figure 2, Space Programming Work Sheet Number 1, has been included to assist in the preparation

Table 1. Building Rule-of-Thumb Area Examples

| | Gross Square Feet Needed | | | | | |
| | Member | | Physician | | Visit | |
Type of HMO	High	Low	High	Low	High	Low
Freestanding ambulatory care only	1.37	0.7	1871	1075	.245	.201
Freestanding center with minimal inpatient care	3.10	2.32	2905	1936	.586	.434
Hospital-based HMO or existing hospital-based ambulatory center	NA*	NA*	NA*	NA*	.270	.228

*Not applicable; examples are for non-prepaid systems.

of a rule-of-thumb space program using the data provided in table 1. The work sheet is used as follows:

1. Complete the top of the form, using the best estimates available for anticipated number of members, physicians, and, using a visit rate, number of total annual visits.

2. Enter the exact values for square feet, high and low, as found in the tables, in the column High/Low.
3. Choose a single value for the square-foot multiplier and enter it in column A, Value Chosen.
4. Enter appropriate values in column B, Quantity, as shown on upper half of the table.

5. Multiply columns A and B to obtain the total gross square feet of the building. Do this for each of the three rows: members, physicians, visits.
6. If desired, average the three values by placing the sum of the three estimates in box C and dividing by 3.

Figure 2. Space Programming Work Sheet No. 1—Building-Type Rule of Thumb

Date _____   Building Type _____
(freestanding, ambulatory, hospital-based)

Assumptions

Number of members _____

Number of physicians _____

Number of annual visits (total) _____

Number of annual visits per member per year _____

Gross Square Foot Estimates

Rule of Thumb	High*	Low*	A Value Chosen	B Quantity	A × B Gross Square Feet, Total	Reason for Selecting A
Square feet/ member				No. of mem.		
Square feet/ physician				No. of physn.		
Square feet/visit				No. of visits		
					C Total of Trial	
				Average value (C ÷ 3 = D)	D	

*See Rule-of-Thumb Area Examples, table 1.

The last column of the work sheet, Reason for Selecting A, is perhaps the most important. Although in this handbook the examples of existing HMO or HMO-type facilities are reduced to three general categories, a great variety exists within these categories for reasons that are important and must be considered. In step 3 above, handbook users must select their own square-foot multipliers for column A in the work sheet.

The quickest way, although the least valid, would be to select the high or low values directly from the tables; or it might seem appropriate just to average the two values. But before doing either, consider that the different rule-of-thumb values result from different levels of service, different ways of delivering service, and different facility configurations. It is impossible to give firm mathematical rules to account for the different values, although some general explanations are easily noted.

Reasons for a higher square-foot multiplier:

- Greater-than-usual range of services, particularly in ancillary areas such as radiology, laboratory, pharmacy
- A facility independent from its affiliated institution and needing greater local service, such as provision for a subscriber office, security, medical records, administration, conference room, health education area, library, dining facilities
- More secondary services provided —areas or rooms assigned to specialties such as allergy, neurology, proctology, urology, emergency facilities, minor surgery, special radiologic or laboratory procedure areas, physical therapy
- Rooms that are large or towards the upper end of generally accepted ranges

- A facility built or renovated in an existing structure—it is more difficult to design efficiently in existing buildings than from scratch
- Unusual geometric configurations —the same design efficiency factor comes into play

Reasons for a lower square-foot multiplier:

- Reduced scope of ancillary services—full radiologic, laboratory, or pharmacy facilities may not be provided at this site
- Reduced level of administrative or support functions
- Specialties not housed locally, or common facilities are shared— there might be a few rooms for medical specialties shared by means of scheduling
- Parsimonious room sizing—for example, examination rooms and consultation rooms may be the same size
- New building, constructed especially for the HMO

The building-type rule-of-thumb method is the simplest and quickest way to grasp the total size of the anticipated facility. It is also the most misleading and most dangerous type of space program because it provides no breakdown of space by departments, no discussions of facility function or operation, and no information on how many examination or consultation rooms are expected. In fact, it is hardly a space program at all. Its value lies in its application to preliminary analyses, feasibility studies, and early budgeting. Once a rule-of-thumb method has yielded a gross building area, that area can be multiplied by an average cost-per-square-foot to give a preliminary estimate of building construction cost.

More accurate data *must* be developed. The facility cannot be designed, the operational and administrative functions cannot be explained, and final budgets cannot be projected without greater detail. A more detailed space program *must* be prepared by using either the simple net-area-to-gross-area method (see page 102) or the department-net-area-to-department-gross-area-to-building-gross-area (see page 103). Both methods begin with the preparation of a net space program, the details of which follow.

Net Space Program

The preparation of a net space program involves six steps, as diagrammed on the Space Programming Flow Chart, figure 3.

1. Prepare a space program sheet for each department (page 90).
2. Select room types to be included in each department (page 91).
3. Determine room sizes (page 91).
4. Determine room quantities (page 92).
5. Calculate net space programs for each department (page 98).
6. Calculate entire net space program (page 98).

Figure 3. Space Programming Flow Chart, Methods 2 and 3

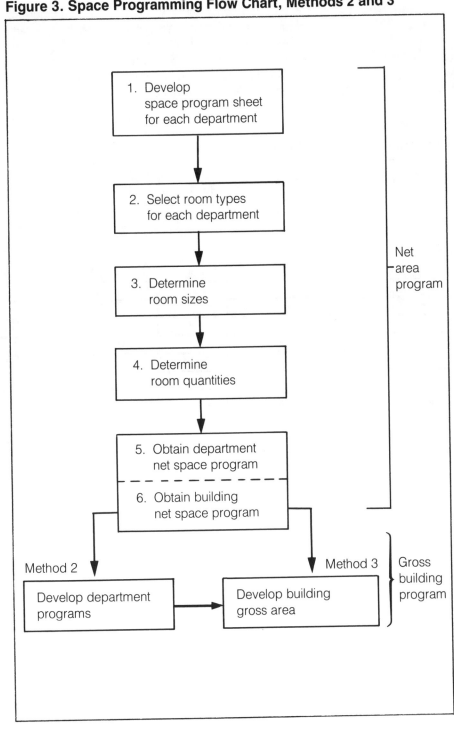

Prepare Space Program Sheet for Each Department

A systematic approach to space programming will save many errors and omissions. An effective way to work is on a departmental basis, where a separate space program is prepared for each department. A sample Departmental Net Area Summary Work Sheet for use during net space programming is shown as a possible format (figure 4). Begin by completing the top part of the work sheet for each department. Department names should follow the same terminology used in the functional program.

Figure 4. Departmental Net Area Summary

Project_____		Building_____	
Department_____		Floor_____	

Room Name or Function	Number of Rooms	Net Room Area	Total Net Square Feet
	ΣR		DN

Select Room Types to Be Included in Each Department

The functional program details the operational requirements for each department, as well as criteria for room use. Each activity or process described in the functional program is studied to determine the kind of physical space appropriate to the activity. Special attention is given to distinguishing activities that require special rooms from activities that may be very different but could occur in the same space.

There are four room types that are difficult to separate: office, consultation, examination, and treatment. The difficulty is primarily in the semantic associations that most physicians and architects have for these words. The space programming team must pay particular attention to defining these four room types on a department-by-department basis. The aim should be to reduce both the number of room types and the room terminology.

Consider, for example, these definitions:

- Office. A room used for *administrative* aspects of providing medical care. The activities may be related to a specific patient, but usually do not require the patient's presence. In other words, *indirect patient care* (for example, charting, record review, telephone consultation).
- Consultation. A room for providing *direct patient care*—the patient and professional are physically together in the room. The patient care activities are primarily limited to *verbal and nonphysical* discussion, investigation, and treatment. Some physical activities that do not require disrobing may be done (blood pressure, oto-ophthalmoscope, and so on).

- Examination. A room for providing *direct patient care*, where physical examination and treatment of the patient are the principal activities. The patient will often be undressed, either partially or completely. Such activity requires a table for the patient to lie or sit on during the examination.
- Treatment. A space for physical examination or treatment of a patient where *special equipment, environment, or professional teams* are required. This is *direct patient care* and will usually involve a patient partially or completely undressed.

Each of these definitions can be summarized in a few key words:

- Office—administrative, indirect patient care
- Consultation—verbal, nonphysical, direct patient care
- Examination—physical, direct patient care
- Treatment—physical, direct patient care, using special materials or personnel

Definitions of other room types (reception, waiting, storage, utility, and so forth) are more easily developed.

Determine Room Sizes

The space programming team will usually recommend room sizes that are reasonable and easily understood. However, if a specific room cannot be easily sized, three actions can be taken:

1. Carefully consider the room's function in relation to some agreed-on standard. For example, suppose that the team cannot decide on the size of an ob-gyn examination room. However, all parties have agreed on the area of a pediatric examination room. Differences in the functions of the two rooms are examined. Because it is desirable to have access to both sides of the patient, and to have additional space at the end of the exam table, the ob-gyn room should be larger.
2. Prepare room layout drawings to scale, positioning all pieces of furniture and equipment and clearly measuring clearances and working space.
3. Make prototypical, full-scale investigations by drawing a full-sized room on the floor and "mocking-up" the room with cardboard walls, or by visiting rooms of different sizes now in use.

Capacity-sized spaces

Although not all rooms can be sized by studying other facilities or similar areas, some can. The activities that occur in a pediatric exam room, for example, are generally so similar that the standard room size will almost always be sufficient. But other rooms house activities that must be larger or smaller, depending on the volume of service occurring there—waiting rooms, pharmacy, laboratory, medical records, secretarial pools, classrooms, and central supply. Guidelines for sizing these spaces are outlined in table 2, Net Room Areas by Capacity.

Table 2. Net Room Areas by Capacity

Site	Area Needed
Lounge	20 square feet per person
Locker	5 square feet per person
Classroom/conference room	20 square feet per person
Secretarial pool	60 square feet per station
Medical record area	2 folders per inch*
Waiting room	15 square feet per person
Recovery	80 square feet per recovery bed
Seated dining	14 square feet per person

*This will vary by type of storage/retrieval system.

Equipment-sized spaces

All rooms must be sized to house the necessary furniture and equipment. In most cases this equipment is based on dimensional standards, so that regardless of manufacturer, exam tables or desks have a common range of sizes. Programmers will proceed directly to room areas when they are confident of standard equipping.

Other equipment, however, may vary greatly in size from manufacturer to manufacturer. In such cases, there is no accurate way to assign the proper area without first obtaining the exact dimensions, clearances, and sizes of the equipment or furniture. During space programming, such rooms should be noted so that special attention can be given to specifying equipment at the earliest possible date. Once selected, manufacturing "cut-sheets" or "rough-in" drawings can be obtained with exact sizes ready for testing on room sheets.

The space programmer should anticipate such equipment-sized rooms in radiology, data processing,

pharmacy (unit dose versus conventional), and special procedure or treatment areas, particularly surgery, proctology, ophthalmology, ENT, dentistry, central supply (sterilizers), food service or kitchens, appointment desks, medical records (type of storage system), and communication systems (telephone switchgear, switchboard, pneumatic tube station, doctors' registry). Floor area should not be the only dimension of interest in equipment-sized spaces; *headroom,* or vertical clearance, for example, is also important, especially when considering a radiology tube track, ceiling-mounted examination or operating lights, wall-hung cabinetry, and counters.

Determine Room Quantities

The actual number of rooms of a particular type can be determined in three ways: direct staff-room correlation, a medical practice standard, or a study of room capacity.

Direct Staff-Room Correlation

A detailed staffing estimate and plan should have been developed as part of the functional program. The facility team can review this staffing program and identify those persons who will require one or more rooms.

In assigning rooms to individuals or positions, the facility team must distinguish between the actual *need* for a separate room and the *desire* for separateness. The possibility of shared or group spaces must be considered, inasmuch as individuals can be housed in less total space if fewer enclosed offices are built, and less space means less construction money.

Acceptable reasons for a separate, private room might include the following:

- Provision of medical care
- Matters of privacy, either personal or fiscal
- Noisy or disruptive activity, such as keypunching, switchboard, pediatric playroom, waiting room

- Special environmental requirements, such as data processing, audio-visual testing (lightproof, soundproof), or lead shielding
- Special equipment

Position, status, or title must also be considered but should also be evaluated in terms of the economics of satisfying the traditional facility benefits. Particular attention should be given to the following:

- Physicians. Should physicians have their own offices? Can their administrative and managerial activities be removed from the medical delivery areas? Can they share space if activities are properly scheduled?
- Paramedical staff (nonphysicians involved in direct patient care, such as mental health counselors, pediatric nurse practitioners, physician's assistants, midwives). How do the activities, equipment needs, or positions of these individuals compare to those of physicians? How will they practice? How are they supervised?
- Administrative personnel. What is their need for privacy, confidentiality, security, or quiet? Must an office be large enough for conferences, or can these take place in a scheduled room serving medical staff, medical education, marketing, or member education?
- Special laws or requirements. City, state, or federal regulations may require that certain individuals or activities be isolated. Accrediting bodies or professional associations may have requirements or guidelines that must be considered.

Medical Practice Standard

It is not uncommon for certain medi-

cal specialties to have a preferred standard for number of rooms. For example, physicians may state that they require two examining rooms and a consultation room, or the ratio may be 3 to 1 (see table 3). The issue here is whether this preference can be justified in the light of patient volume and visit length, physician schedule, and construction cost.

Stated standards should be taken into consideration as important statements of user need, but they must also be subject to a quantitative analysis.

Room Capacity

The least subjective method of determining room quantity and complement is to compare the capacity of a facility with the anticipated load or demand. Such studies take time, and base data is extremely difficult to

obtain, but the analysis is likely to offer a more comprehensive and reliable estimate than the rule-of-thumb method. These studies also demand a comprehensive evaluation of how the HMO will deliver its services.

Five variables are at issue:

1. What activities occur?
2. How often do they occur?
3. Where do they occur?
4. How long do they take?
5. How efficiently are they done? (For example, take into account down time, clean-up, or standby capacity.)

The Patient Encounter Work Sheet, Part I, Loading (figure 5), which was prepared in order to assist in the development of room capacity information, has been organized to allow a capacity study of examination and consultation rooms in the medical care areas, but with minor changes it can be adjusted to other room types.

Table 3. Number of Examination Rooms per Consultation Room*

Specialty	High	Low	Median**
Medicine or General Practice	3.4	1.1	2.0
Pediatrics	3.8	1.5	2.3
Obstetrics-Gynecology	2.0	1.0	1.6
Consulting-Surgical Specialty	4.0	2.0	2.1
Consulting-Medical Specialty	4.0	1.5	1.8

*Values taken from the 12 sample plans.
**Median = the value where there are as many individual cases with the higher values as lower. It is the middle case, not the average.

Figure 5. Patient Encounter Work Sheet—Part 1, Loading

	A	B	Z	C	D	E	F	G	H	J		
	Total No. of Visits	Patient Visits	No. of Annual Visits by Type (A × B)	Resource Utilization						Annual Demand*		
				Consultation		Examination		Treatment		Consult	Exam	Treat
Specialty		Type / % of Total		% of Patients Using Room	Length of Time Used*	% of Patients Using Room	Length of Time Used*	% of Patients Using Room	Length of Time Used*	ZxCxD	ZxExF	ZxGxH

*In minutes.

In addition to the work sheet, summary information is presented in two additional tables (tables 4 and 5), which are based on a time-motion study conducted on 1,600 patient visits in a single health maintenance organization.[1] These data can form the basis for estimates in completing the Patient Encounter Work Sheet (figure 5).

1. What activities occur? The facility team should carefully diagram the different types of patient visits, or the reasons for visiting the HMO facility. Visits should be described in detail, categorizing visit types to specialty areas, such as medicine and pediatrics. This categorization cannot be resolved by the facility team alone but should have the cooperation of the medical staff and administrative and other members of the organization team. Categories should be based on the patients' requirements for different combinations of staff and facilities. For example, an initial medical history and physical for a new enrollee will take more time than renewal of a birth control prescription. Some episodic visits can be handled without a physical examination, whereas others will require consultation and a physical with the physician.

Visit types that would work for most ambulatory visits might include first visit or intake, consultation, examination, treatment, annual/periodic exam, well-person care, and follow-up care.

The question that should be asked in establishing visit categories is, "Can one differentiate the categories by the amount of time required in the examination, consultation, or treatment room, as well as the time with the physician, physician's assistant, or nurse?" If a clear and estimable difference can be demonstrated, then a category can be established.

In addition, a patient visit list has value beyond space programming. In an operational appointment system, for example, a patient who calls for an annual physical can have a larger block of time reserved in the physician's schedule. Likewise, at later stages in the HMO's operation, the patient visit distinction can provide valuable insight into the efficiency and actual use of the HMO.

If it is too difficult to differentiate visit types, room capacity can be determined by distinguishing between staff utilization and room utilization on a specialty basis.

Table 4. Use of Building Sites by HMO Patients

Site	% of Patients		
	Pediatrics	Medicine	Ob/Gyn
Waiting Room	85.5	93.2	96.8
Consultation Room	27.9	70.5	93.0
Examination Room	94.4	75.6	90.4
Radiology	2.2	13.0	2.0
Laboratory	3.8	27.8	14.0
Pharmacy	26.0	29.5	44.7

Table 5. Mean Minutes: Use of Building Sites by HMO Patients

(Mean minutes of use when used; see tables 3 and 4)

Site	Pediatrics	Medicine	Ob/Gyn
Waiting Room	8.6	19.3	14.9
Consultation Room	11.9	12.2	9.1
Examination Room	34.8	17.7	10.8
Radiology	25.6	33.9	19.5
Laboratory	23.0	9.8	6.1
Pharmacy	15.9	18.7	14.5
Total Visits	57.6	53.8	42.8

2. How often do the activities occur? Once the patient visits have been identified, some estimate should be made of the frequency of each visit type for each specialty; a percent of total visits to each specialty is sufficient. (For example, 10 percent of all visits to surgery are annual check-ups, 40 percent are follow-ups; see column B, figure 5.)

3. Where do the activities occur? Each visit type should be analyzed to estimate the percent of patients who will go to a particular type room—for each visit category, how many patients will use the consultation, examination, or treatment rooms? There should be great variation; if there is not, the visit categories should be reviewed to see whether some categories can be combined. (Figure 5, columns C, E, and G.)

4. How long do the activities take? The average length of time (in minutes) that a patient stays in a given room must be estimated for each visit type. Base this on the time the patient spends in the room, not the time the physician spends with the patient, which is invariably less. A patient may dress, wait, or be prepared without a physician or other health provider present, but an occupied room, with or without the physician, is not available to other uses. (Columns D, F, H.)

On the basis of these four questions—what, how often, where, and how long—Part I of the Patient Encounter Work Sheet (figure 5) can be completed, yielding the total number of minutes that all patients will occupy each room type. (Follow the work sheet directions.) These totals (column J) can be considered the annual demand for each room type.

The programming team must now determine the ability of the facilities to process this demand: what capacity is required? The number of spe-

cific rooms required will vary, depending on the efficiency with which a facility can move the patients through rooms.

5. How efficiently can the demand be met? The three governing factors here are the hours of facility operations, standby or overflow capacity, and down time between patients.

Part II of the Patient Encounter Work Sheet, Capacity (figure 6), compares the three efficiency factors to the total demand generated in Part I (figure 5).

Columns A and B, hours of operation and annual minutes available, simply compute the total time during a year that the HMO will be open on a full-service basis. During these hours, the facility has a capacity to meet the normal service demand. The number of hours of weekly full-time operation (column A) is multiplied by 52 weeks and then by 60 minutes (column B) to obtain the number of minutes of regular service in a single year.

Column E represents a consideration of how much extra room capacity is desirable above the "normal" or average daily load. There will be busy days and slow days. The questions that must be asked here are:

- How much will daily load fluctuate? A range of 160-240 patients per day (mean = 200) represents a maximum demand or standby capacity of 20 percent or 0.20.
- What are the consequences of insufficient capacity? Most often, the clearest result is longer patient waiting times. Obviously, it is uneconomical to design a system for no waiting. Generally, it is desirable to meet some percentage of the possible delays that may occur on above-average days. If a decision is made to handle a 50 percent

overflow (above average) without a backup, 50 percent of 240 - 200 = 20, and the standby factor is 10 percent (20 patients in 200) or 0.10.

- What are the risks of an undercapacity? This varies by specialty. For example, it is highly desirable to have enough delivery rooms in a hospital to handle a very high percentage of anticipated simultaneous demand. It may be less dangerous to not satisfy the maximum simultaneous demand for a pediatric examination room.

Generally it becomes increasingly expensive, in a non-linear fashion, to decrease the probability of temporarily running short of space. In theory, infinite expense is required to provide sufficient room resources for all possible loading conditions, whereas a very small increase in facility cost may accommodate 20 or 30 percent overflow without backup.

Column C, the efficiency factor, is used to account for facility down time. Although this factor is difficult to pin down in medical facilities, a method for determining the down time and standby rates has been established.[2]

The major elements that determine room efficiency are room use, practice pattern, room preparation, and simple inefficiency.

- The demand for room time calculated in figure 5 was described as minutes of patient use. Some rooms that are used to deliver direct patient care are also used for other purposes and therefore are not fully available. Consider a physician office/consultation room, used by the physician to carry on certain administrative and nondirect patient care activities. Clearly, if one-half of the room's day is used for these activities, only 50 percent (0.5)

Figure 6. Patient Encounter Work Sheet—Part 2, Capacity

Specialty	**A** Hours per Week of Full-Time Operation	**B** Annual Minutes Available (A × 60 × 52)*	**C** Efficiency Factor — Consult	Exam	Treat	**D** Annual Demand** — Consult	Exam	Treat	**E** Standby Capacity — Consult	Exam	Treat	**F** No. of Rooms Required*** — Consult	Exam	Treat

*No. of hours per week (column A) × 60 (minutes per hour) × 52 (weeks per year) = no. minutes per year.

**Take from figure 5, column J.

$$***F = \frac{D + (D \times E)}{C} \div B$$

remains to meet patient demand.

- The organization of the practice affects room utilization. A good example is the practice of lining up pediatric patients in examination rooms so that they are undressed and ready for examination when the physician arrives. This may reduce physician idle time, but it increases the occupancy rate of pediatric examination rooms, because patients are involved in activities in the examination room that in other specialties occur in the waiting room. The efficiency rates of pediatric rooms are lower than those in general medicine and obstetrics. More examination rooms are required in pediatrics than in other specialties to meet the needs of an equal number of visits.
- Some rooms need to be prepared or cleaned before and after patient use, and during this time they are unavailable to meet patient demand. The longer the prep time or clean-up time, the lower the efficiency factor. Patient preparation time also varies by specialty; it takes longer to prepare a patient for a pelvic than for stethoscopic examination.
- Few practices are capable of operating at 100 percent efficiency. People must eat and take other breaks, rooms must be maintained and repaired. If a building is open for ten hours a day and an examination room is assigned to a doctor who works eight hours with one hour for lunch, the efficiency factor of that room begins at 70 percent (0.7). Patients would probably not be admitted to the room during the three hours the physician was not present.

There are no standards for determining the efficiency of an HMO room. However, as indicated in table 6, Room Efficiency, which shows

room efficiency in one HMO, these factors are likely to be much less than expected. Be extremely wary of rule-of-thumb capacity indications.

The following rules can be relied on:

- Consultation rooms are less efficient than examination rooms.
- Efficiency factors higher than 40 percent must be justified.
- Primary care rooms have higher efficiency rates than specialty care rooms.
- Combination rooms (examination/consultation or examination/treatment rooms) have higher efficiency factors than single-purpose rooms.

Calculate a Net Space Program for Each Department

The Departmental Net Area Summary, figure 4, can now be fully completed with the information obtained above. A departmental net space program includes the name of each room, the number of rooms, and the net area of

the rooms. Add the final column to obtain the total net square feet (DN) for each department.

Calculate Entire Net Space Program

The net area program for each department can now be summed to determine the estimated net area of the facility. This should be done on one of the two Building Gross Area Determination Work Sheets, method 2 (figure 7) or method 3 (figure 8). Each department name should be entered in the appropriate column. The net area of each department (as it appears on figure 4) should be entered in the column labeled DN, or departmental net area. Add this column to obtain the total net building area (BN).

Do not complete any other information on these sheets at this time; other items relate to a determination of the gross building area.

As a check, compute the percentage of total net space that each

Table 6. Room Efficiency: A Single Study

Percent of available time (hours of full-time operation) that rooms are occupied by patients (with or without MD present). Based on 1,600 patient visits.

Specialty	Consultation Room	Examination Room
General Medicine	29.5%	31.7%
Pediatrics	10.2%	50.9%
Obstetrics/Gynecology	31.7%	30.6%

Source: Reuter, L.F. Programming ambulatory care facilities and staff. *Medical Care.* 1974 Jan.-Feb. 12(1)

Figure 7. Building Gross Area Determination Work Sheet, Method 2

Project _____   Building _____

Simple Net-Area-to-Gross-Area: A Building-Wide Survey

Department	Department Net Area (DN)
	BN = ΣDN

Building Net Area (BN) × Building Net-to-Gross Multiplier
= Building Gross (BG)

BG

Figure 8. Building Gross Area Determination Work Sheet, Method 3

Project _____   Building _____

Net-Area-to-Departmental-Gross-Area-to-Building-Gross-Area: A Department-Wide Survey

Department	DN*	DN:DG* Multiplier	DG
	BN		ΣDG

*Department Net Area
**Department-Net-to-Department-Gross

Department Gross-Building Gross Ratio = DG/BG =

Department Gross-Building Gross Multiplier = $\dfrac{1}{DG/BG}$ =

Building Gross Area (BG) = DG × DG-to-BG Multiplier (above) = BG   BG

department accounts for and compare it to the ranges shown in table 7, Breakdown of Net Space in 6 HMO Facilities.

Programming Gross Building Area for the HMO

Two different methods can be used in moving from a net space program to a gross building area program, as demonstrated in the Space Programming Flow Chart (see figure 3). Either direct extension from the net space program by a net-area-to-gross-area multiplier (method 2) or the determination of gross building area by an intermediate area program, the departmental gross area program (method 3), will suffice. Both are discussed here, and the starting point for both is the net space program already developed.

Table 7. Breakdown of Net Space in 6 HMO Facilities (Freestanding Ambulatory Only)

Department	Percent of Building Net Space		
	High	Low	Median**
Family practice*	39.0	28.0	38.5
General medicine	20.6	12.7	15.7
Pediatrics	16.0	7.7	10.5
Obstetrics/Gynecology	6.4	5.1	5.8
Surgical specialties	10.3	2.5	8.0
Medical specialties	11.2	7.4	8.0
Radiology	10.5	5.0	5.4
Laboratory	7.6	2.4	4.0
Pharmacy	8.0	3.2	5.3
Urgent visit	6.4	3.0	5.4
Psychiatry*	—	—	0.9
Dental*	18.0	8.7	13.7
Administration	32.0	10.4	17.9
Physical therapy*	4.3	1.4	4.0

*Not all six facilities contained these departments.
**Median = the value where one-half of the examples have higher multipliers and one-half have lower multipliers. It is not the average.

Building Net-Area-to-Gross-Area Method

The net area of a building is only part of the total area necessary to house those net spaces; numerous nonprogrammed spaces are added to the net area to obtain the complete or gross building area. The simplest way to make the adjustment is to choose a reliable multiplier of net area.

The work sheet for method 2, Building Gross Area Determination (figure 7), is used in making this conversion. Department names and net areas are brought forward from the Departmental Net Area Summary, figure 4.

The table of Building Net-Area-to-Gross-Area Multipliers (table 8) is based on a study of 12 HMO-type facilities. There are considerable variations and many reasons to account for them.

Selection of the net-area-to-gross-area multiplier requires careful consideration. No specific rules can be formulated to select the "best" multiplier, but the following considerations generally come into play.

Reasons for a higher multiplier:

- The building is a renovated or reused facility.
- The building will have more than a single floor.
- The structural system has short spans or irregular spans.
- Extra space must be supplied for mechanical equipment rooms (boilers, air conditioners, and so forth).
- The space program consists of many small rooms. For example, many small waiting areas rather than one large room.
- The site or zoning laws require irregular or nonrectangular facilities.

- More specialized or technical services will be provided (nursing units, nuclear medicine, and so forth).
- Separate staff and public corridors will be a criterion in the design.

Reasons for a lower multiplier:

- The facility is a new building designed for the HMO.
- The structural systems consist of longer and more regular spans.
- "Multi-use" or "multi-person" corridors are planned for patient, staff, and material circulation.
- Mechanical services or administrative and technical medical services will not be included in the facility but obtained elsewhere.
- There are many large rooms.
- There will be a minimum of differentiation between separate areas in the building—room size and building layout are regular and repetitive from department to department.

The selection of a net-area-to-gross-area multiplier is one of the most important decisions in space programming. The consequences of an error on the low side are much more serious than an overestimation and always result in (1) a construction budget that is too small, (2) selection of a site or facility that cannot house the intended function, and (3) a lengthy and trying period of design and reprogramming as an attempt is made to "shoehorn" the functions into insufficient area.

It is strongly recommended that the net-area-to-gross-area multiplier chosen be at least equal to the table median, preferably higher. Budgets and programs can always be cut back later. Begin on the high side.

To determine the final building gross area (BG) using this method, choose the desired multiplier and increase the building net area (BN on method 2 work sheet, figure 7) by direct multiplication.

Table 8. Building Net-Area-to-Gross-Area Multipliers in 12 HMO-Type Facilities

Building Type	Building Net-to-Gross Multipliers		
	High	Low	Median*
Freestanding (ambulatory services only)	1.99	1.37	1.78
Freestanding ambulatory plus inpatient services (including bed units)	2.01	1.85	1.93
Hospital-based (ambulatory portion only)	1.98	1.43	1.78

*Median = the value where one-half of the examples have higher multipliers and one-half have lower multipliers. It is not the average.

As a final check, it may be wise to test this building gross against the member-, physician-, or visit-per-square-foot ratios presented in the building rule-of-thumb method described earlier in this chapter, or by the more technical method 3, below.

Department-Net-Area-to-Department-Gross-Area-to-Building-Gross-Area Method

Method 3 is designed to provide a more detailed analysis of the factors that determine a net-area-to-gross-area multiplier, based on the fact that the net area of certain departments can be designed or constructed with more efficiency than others: 1,000 net square feet of one department can be laid out in a smaller building gross area than 1,000 net square feet of a different department.

The Building Gross Area Determination Work Sheet for method 3, figure 8, outlines the mechanics of this more-detailed programming technique. The department names and programmed departmental net areas (DN) are brought forward from the Departmental Net Area Summary, figure 4. Each department is then studied independently to determine an appropriate multiplier that can be used to estimate the departmental area.

Table 9, Departmental Net-Area-to-Gross-Area Multipliers, partially explains the variances in these multipliers. Notice the progression from large, open spaces with small multipliers to the many-roomed, more technically equipped medical-care spaces that have higher multipliers. Bearing in mind the general discussion of choosing various space programming multipliers (methods 1 and

2), study your own space and functional program and select a multiplier for each individual department on the method 3 work sheet (figure 8). Determine the corresponding departmental area by multiplying the departmental net (DN) times the DN-to-DG multiplier. Add the DG column to obtain the total of all departmental gross areas (DG) in the building.

Table 9. Departmental Net-Area-to-Gross-Area Multipliers in 12 HMO-Type Facilities

Department or Area	Departmental Net-to-Gross Multipliers		
	High	Low	Median*
Lobby	1.58	1.01	1.10
Pharmacy	1.18	1.03	1.10
Supply	1.20	1.10	1.13
Laboratory	1.39	1.03	1.15
Administration	1.33	1.05	1.20
Psychiatry	1.46	1.10	1.30
Consulting-Medical Specialty	1.44	1.17	1.27
Urgent Visit	1.52	1.23	1.39
Pediatrics	1.48	1.33	1.39
Consulting-Surgical Specialty	1.51	1.35	1.40
Medicine	1.58	1.31	1.44
Radiology	1.57	1.21	1.45
Obstetrics	1.57	1.28	1.46
Dental	1.60	1.28	1.49

*Median = the value where one-half of the examples have higher multipliers and one-half have lower multipliers. It is not the average.

The transition from departmental gross area (DG) to building gross area (BG) is similar to the net-area-to-building-gross transformation of method 2. A single multiplier is chosen, based on the criteria discussed in method 2. Table 10, Departmental-Gross-to-Building-Gross Multipliers, presents representative data.

References

1. Reuter, L.F. Programming ambulatory care facilities and staff. *Medical Care.* 1974 Jan.-Feb. 12(1).
2. McDonald, L.K., and Reuter, L.F. A patient-specific approach to hospital cost accounting. *Health Services Research.* 1973 Summer, 8(2).

Table 10. Departmental-Gross-Area-to-Building-Gross-Area Multipliers in 12 HMO-Type Facilities

Building Type	Departmental-Gross-to-Building-Gross Multipliers		
	High	Low	Median*
Freestanding (ambulatory services only)	1.45	1.10	1.35
Freestanding ambulatory plus inpatient services (including nursery unit)	1.49	1.29	1.39
Hospital-based (ambulatory portion only)	1.44	1.10	1.41

*Median = the value where one-half of the examples have higher multipliers and one-half have lower multipliers. It is not the average.

Appendix B

Space Determinants

Facility space programs are influenced by "key space generators" (Hayward et al., 1985, p. 5), such as anticipated work load, projected staffing, space requirements of special equipment, and institutional policies affecting space requirements (see chapter 8, Analysis). This appendix is designed to assist the programmer in identifying appropriate key space generators for selected ambulatory care spaces and, where appropriate, to suggest sizes and quantities for these spaces.

Anticipated work load projections (such as the number of annual procedures expected during a given year) can be translated into the number of workstations required to accommodate anticipated demand. This involves a three-step process:

1. Identify appropriate *key space generators* (see table 1).
2. Identify required quantity and size of *primary activity spaces* by determining their *productivity rates* in relation to key space generators (see table 2).
3. Identify quantity and size of *support and administration spaces* needed to complete the functional space program (see table 3).

If 4,200 annual procedures (key space generator) are projected for an ambulatory surgery facility, and 1 operating room (primary activity space) can accommodate approximately 1,355 annual procedures (productivity rate), then 4,200 divided by 1,355, or 3.10, operating rooms are required. In this case 3 operating rooms would be programmed.

Figure 22 on page 64 (Example of Calculations to Determine Space Needs) illustrates the process of determining productivity rates for an outpatient operating room. It is important to note that a number of variables, which may differ at any given facility, influence the productivity rate. These variables, which include hours of operation, average length of procedures by type, average duration of clean-up and set-up time, and scheduling inefficiencies, must be worked into the calculations if reliable numbers are to be generated.

Once the required number of primary activity spaces are determined, support and administration spaces can be added.

Important:

The data that follows should be used as preliminary guidelines only! Programming requirements of specific facilities may vary from these guidelines. All applicable code requirements should be thoroughly researched to avoid conflicts, keeping in mind that code *minimums* do not necessarily reflect *ideal* conditions.

The selected spaces addressed in tables 1 through 3 in no way imply "complete" space programs. Instead, a few spaces are discussed as a point of departure for developing more comprehensive space programs. The extent of spaces included in any program should reflect the unique requirements of the facility being programmed.

Table 1. Key Space Generators by Type of Service

Table 1 identifies the type of work load data that generally influence functional area requirements of the selected health care services listed below. (See table 2 for productivity rate guidelines.)

Type of Health Care Service	Key Space Generators	Remarks
Urgent Care	• Visits/year & day • Visits/hour during 4-hour peak period • % of total visits/day seen during 4-hour peak period • Type of visit by % • Average duration of visit by type (actual time spent in exam-treatment room plus clean-up & set-up time) • % of scheduled versus drop-in visits • Hours & days of operation • Special equipment • Levels of care provided • Staffing • Affiliation with back-up facilities (if applicable)	Assume facility is not intended for life-threatening illness or injury.
General Medicine (Family Practice, Outpatient Clinics, and so forth)	• Visits/year, day, & hour • Peak work load & average work load • Type of visit by % • Average duration of visit by type (actual time spent in exam-treatment room plus clean-up & set-up time) • % of scheduled versus drop-in visits • Hours & days of operation • Special equipment • Special service provided (x-ray, laboratory, and so forth) • Shared areas and/or equipment (if applicable) • Staffing	

(continued)

Table 1. Key Space Generators by Type of Service (continued)

Type of Health Care Service	Key Space Generators	Remarks
Ambulatory Surgery	• Procedures/year & day • Type of procedure by % • Average duration of procedure by type (procedure time plus clean-up & set-up time) • Hours & days of operation • Special procedures performed • Special equipment • Staffing • Relationship to inpatient surgery program (if applicable)	If high-risk outpatient procedures are performed in an affiliated inpatient surgery facility, those procedures should be excluded from the work load calculations.
Clinical Laboratory	• Test/year, day, & hour • Type of test by % • Peak work load & average work load • Average duration of test by type (duration of test & turnaround time) • % of STAT versus routine tests • Hours & days of operation • Degree of automation • Special equipment & related batch testing capabilities • Staffing • Relationship to other affiliated laboratory (if applicable)	If the facility being programmed is part of a network of satellite laboratories, identify which facilities collect and which process specimens. This will influence the number, type, and size of spaces required. Because instrument technology is advancing at a tremendous pace, productivity rate guidelines quickly become outdated. Therefore, verify all planning guidelines before applying them.
Diagnostic Imaging	• Procedures/year, month, & day • Type of procedure by % • Peak work load & average work load • Average duration of procedure by type (procedure time plus clean-up & set-up time) • % of scheduled versus unscheduled procedures • Hours & days of operation • Special procedures & equipment (computed tomography, magnetic resonance imaging, and so forth) • Type and location of film storage • Method of film retrieval • Staffing	Because instrument technology and the development of new diagnostic procedures and record storage systems are advancing at a tremendous pace, productivity rate guidelines quickly become outdated. Therefore, verify all planning guidelines before applying them.

(continued)

Table 1. Key Space Generators by Type of Service (continued)

Type of Health Care Service	Key Space Generators	Remarks
Physical Therapy	• Visits/year & day • Type of visit by % • Modalities/year & day • Average duration of modality by type • Hours & days of operation • Special equipment	
Fitness Center	• Visits/year & day • Number of members (if applicable) • Average duration of visit • Peak work load & average work load • Special equipment by type • Staffing	
Pharmacy	• Orders/year & day • Type of orders by % • Average turnaround time per order, by type • Hours & days of operation • Degree of automation • System of storing and replenishing stock • Method of accessing medical records (if applicable) • Relationship to affiliated inpatient pharmacy and/or affiliated satellite pharmacies (if applicable)	

Table 2. Productivity Rates of Selected Primary Activity Spaces

Table 2 suggests a range of numerical values to be used as productivity rates for selected primary activity spaces. Where applicable, net room area guidelines are also suggested. As with all data in this appendix, these values should be used as preliminary guidelines only. Applications to specific facilities may vary considerably.

Room Description	Activity Space Productivity Rate Guidelines	Net Room Area Guidelines	Remarks
Examination-Treatment Room (Urgent Care)	Assume an average of 0.8-1.2 visits per multipurpose exam-treatment room per hour. Room utilization is likely to be lower during slow periods and higher during peak periods. Assume an average visit duration (time that patient spends in exam-treatment room plus clean-up and set-up time) of 30 minutes. If exam-treatment rooms are specialized (gynecology, ENT, and so forth) more rooms may be required than if rooms are all capable of multipurpose use.	Assume 80-120 NSF for general-purpose exam-treatment area. Will vary by specialty. May be larger for special treatment and special equipment.	Rates of room utilization will vary greatly by type of visit (medical, minor injury, OB-GYN, ENT, and so forth). Because urgent care visits usually are not scheduled, room utilization projections must allow for peak periods and for visits that are considerably longer than average.
Examination-Treatment Room (General Medicine)	Assume an average of 2-4 visits per general-purpose exam-treatment room per hour for routine scheduled appointments. Assume 1-4 exam-treatment rooms per consultation room. This will vary based on how the practice is organized (see "Remarks" and table 3, appendix A). Assume 2-3 general-purpose exam-treatment rooms per physician.	Assume 80-120 NSF for general-purpose exam-treatment rooms. Will vary by specialty. May be larger for special treatment and special equipment.	Room utilization rates will vary by type of visit and by the policies of individual practices. For example, does consultation occur in the exam room or does the patient go to a consultation room after the examination?

(continued)

Table 2. Productivity Rates of Selected Primary Activity Spaces (continued)

Room Description	Activity Space Productivity Rate Guidelines	Net Room Area Guidelines	Remarks
Operating Room (Ambulatory Surgery)	Assume 1,300-1,820 procedures per operating room per year.[1] This will vary considerably based on the percentage of each type of procedure performed. Assume a minimum of 3,000 surgical procedures per year and a minimum of two operating rooms per dedicated ambulatory facility.[2]	Although some codes allow outpatient operating rooms to be smaller than inpatient operating rooms (270 NSF minimum versus 360 NSF minimum in some jurisdictions), 400 NSF is often suggested for general-purpose in- and outpatient operating rooms to allow a variety of special equipment to be used. Check applicable code requirements.	An efficiently managed surgery center that only serves outpatients may have the potential to accommodate 50-60% more procedures per room per year than a similarly sized inpatient surgery department, due to shorter average procedure time, shorter average recovery time, and the absence of unscheduled emergency surgeries. However, this increased capacity assumes a steady case load to ensure efficient room utilization. Therefore, a careful determination of anticipated procedures by type must be made to determine actual utilization rates (see figures 21 & 22, chapter 8).
Recovery Room (Ambulatory Surgery)	Assume 1-2 recovery beds per operating room if an additional second-stage recovery area is provided.[1] 1 isolation recovery bed per 10 recovery beds has been suggested.[3]	Assume 80-120 NSF per recovery bed, exclusive of nurse station and storage areas. Check applicable code requirements. Assume about 160 NSF per isolation recovery bed.[3]	If a large pediatric case load is anticipated, a separate pediatric recovery area is recommended. The number of beds is determined by the percentage of pediatric procedures anticipated.

(continued)

Table 2. Productivity Rates of Selected Primary Activity Spaces (continued)

Room Description	Activity Space Productivity Rate Guidelines	Net Room Area Guidelines	Remarks
Preoperative Patient Preparation & Holding Area (Ambulatory Surgery)	Assume 1-2 pre-op holding beds per operating room.	Assume 40-80 NSF per pre-op holding bed. Area requirements vary based on the use of individual cubicles versus group areas. Note: a variety of satisfactory pre-op room arrangements exist, each with specific area requirements.	Often a multifunctional pre-op & recovery area can be implemented, with most beds used for pre-op in the morning, recovery in the afternoon, as the demand shifts. Although this arrangement can increase staffing efficiency, it must be coordinated with functional and staffing policies. If a large pediatric case load is anticipated, a separate pediatric prep area may be desired (see "Remarks" under Recovery Room, above).
Clinical Laboratory	Because tests that do not require a rapid response are often "batch processed," high-volume equipment is sometimes used. Many instruments perform numerous tests simultaneously. Although such tests may take only a few seconds, they tend not to be run continuously, sometimes only once a day or even once a week.	In very general terms, assume 60 NSF per one-person workstation plus area required for special floor-mounted equipment (include adequate area for servicing equipment, where applicable).	Size and work load capabilities vary greatly based on the extent of services performed. Productivity rates are influenced significantly by the capabilities of special equipment.*

(continued)

Table 2. Productivity Rates of Selected Primary Activity Spaces (continued)

Room Description	Activity Space Productivity Rate Guidelines	Net Room Area Guidelines	Remarks
Radiography (Diagnostic Imaging)	Assume 20 general radiographic procedures and 6-10.5 general fluoroscopic procedures per room per 8-hour shift.[4] Room productivity levels will vary greatly by type of procedure. For example, a mammography room can accommodate fewer procedures per shift than a general radiographic room.	Room dimensions may vary by type and capability of equipment. Assume 250-300 NSF for a general-purpose radiographic room, including control area and electrical equipment (transformers and so forth). May vary with special equipment.	
Ultrasound (Diagnostic Imaging)	Assume 2,200 procedures per room per year.[5] This translates to 8-9 procedures per room per day if the facility is open 255 days per year.	Assume 100-120 NSF per procedure room.	Provide direct access to dedicated patient toilet room.
Nuclear Medicine (Diagnostic Imaging)	Assume 2,200 procedures per room per year.[5] This translates to 8-9 procedures per room per day if the facility is open 255 days per year.	Room dimensions will vary greatly depending on type of equipment and number of cameras per room. Assume 200-250 NSF for a general-purpose procedure room with 1 camera.	Provide "Hot Lab" within or adjacent to procedure room. Provide patient toilet accessible from or adjacent to procedure room.

(continued)

Table 2. Productivity Rates of Selected Primary Activity Spaces (continued)

Room Description	Activity Space Productivity Rate Guidelines	Net Room Area Guidelines	Remarks
Computed Tomography (Diagnostic Imaging)	Assume 2,500-3,000 procedures per room per year.[5] This translates to 9-12 procedures per room per day if the facility is open 255 days per year.	Size of CT suite will vary depending on the number and type of support and administration spaces programmed, as well as the number and type of CT units included. Assume 360-400 NSF for a general-purpose full body scan procedure room. Allow an additional 180-220 NSF for control room and 80-120 NSF for computer room. Check applicable code and equipment requirements.	
Magnetic Resonance Imaging (Diagnostic Imaging)	Assume 2,000 procedures per year (minimum) to justify equipment and facility costs of an MRI suite with one procedure room. This translates to about 7-8 procedures per room per day based on 255 operational days per year. (Note: equipment maintenance and down time will affect the amount of procedure time available. Consult manufacturers and other users of similar equipment for guidelines.) Procedure duration will vary by type. Assume in very general terms an average duration of 1.1-1.3 hours, including clean-up and set-up time.	MRI scan rooms vary from 550 NSF to over 1,000 NSF. Space requirements vary by manufacturer, magnet strength, shielding requirements, and many other influences. Although mobile truck-mounted MRI suites are as small as 400 GSF,† many "fixed" installations with one procedure room range anywhere from 3,500-4,500 GSF† per suite. The basic components of an MRI suite include scan room, control room, computer room, storage area, viewing room, and a variety of patient and staff spaces. Cryogen storage often is part of the procedure room.	Magnetic resonance imaging technology is still in its early developmental stages. As a result, planning guidelines may change rapidly. Space requirements vary from one manufacturer to another. For detailed site planning and facility planning guidelines, contact the appropriate manufacturer's representative.

(continued)

Table 2. Productivity Rates of Selected Primary Activity Spaces (continued)

Room Description	Activity Space Productivity Rate Guidelines	Net Room Area Guidelines	Remarks
Cardiac Catheterization (Diagnostic Imaging)	Assume 3-5 procedures per room per day for a busy facility.[6] Assume that down time may amount to 1 day per 2-4 weeks. Assume 200-400 procedures per year (minimum) should be performed to maintain skills and efficiency of physician and staff.[7]	Size of the procedure room will vary based on type of equipment used and extent of procedures performed. Assume a range of 360 NSF (minimum) to 560 NSF (elaborate) per procedure room.	
Pharmacy	Assume 12 minutes per prescription: 8 minutes for dispensing, 4 minutes for counseling.[8] Assume 35-40 prescriptions per day per dispensing station: 5 prescriptions per hour, 8 hours per day. Number of workstations required = (annual prescriptions × average duration [in minutes] per prescription) ÷ (daily hours of operation × annual days of operation x 60 minutes per hour).	Assume 80 NSF per workstation for outpatient dispensing.[8] Assume 60 NSF per workstation for compounding.	These planning guidelines assume the pharmacy is independent from inpatient pharmacies and serves only outpatients.

(continued)

Table 2. Productivity Rates of Selected Primary Activity Spaces (continued)

Room Description	Activity Space Productivity Rate Guidelines	Net Room Area Guidelines	Remarks
Physical Therapy	Assume 18-22 visits per physical therapist per day. Average duration of visit will vary greatly by type.	Assume 80 NSF per treatment cubicle. Assume 140-160 NSF per exercise workstation, 400 NSF minimum for total exercise area. Exercise workstation areas will vary, based on equipment requirements.	

1. Burns, L. *Ambulatory Surgery.* Rockville, MD: Aspen Systems Corp., 1984, p. 114.
2. *Evaluation and Space Programming Methodology Series, Vol. 2: Surgery/Day Surgery Suite.* Canada: Minister of Health and Welfare, 1978, pp. 34-35.
3. *Evaluation and Space Programming Methodologies.* Canada: Minister of Health and Welfare, 1984, p. 20.13.
4. Committee on Department Planning, Commission on Radiologic Equipment and Facilities. *Planning Guide for Radiologic Installations, Fascicle 4: Basic Concepts.* Chicago, IL: American College of Radiology, 1977, p. 31.
5. *Evaluation and Space Programming Methodologies.* Canada: Minister of Health and Welfare, 1984, p. 12.13.
6. Laufman, H., ed. *Hospital Special Care Facilities: Planning for User Needs.* New York City: Academic Press, 1981, p. 472.
7. *Evaluation and Space Programming Methodology Series, Vol. 18: Special Imaging Services.* Canada: Minister of Health and Welfare, 1981, p. 25.
8. *Evaluation and Space Programming Methodologies.* Canada: Minister of Health and Welfare, 1984, pp. 15.2 and 15.11.

* For more detailed planning data, see *Medical Laboratory Planning and Design.* Skokie, IL: College of American Pathologists, 1985.
† GSF (gross square feet) represents the total area occupied by a group or suite of rooms, including walls and corridors, in contrast to the net square feet (NSF) of a particular room, which does not include walls or corridors.

Table 3. Space Determinants of Selected Support and Administrative Spaces

Table 3 is not intended to represent a comprehensive list of support and administrative spaces. Instead, some typical spaces are discussed as a point of departure, for developing space programs tailored to the needs of specific facilities.

Area Description	Space Programming Guidelines	Remarks
Waiting area	15 NSF/seat Assume 25-30 NSF/exam-treatment room	80 NSF minimum
Interview/admitting cubicle	40-50 NSF/cubicle Assume 1 cubicle/10,000 annual primary care visits*	
Dictation cubicle	20 NSF/seat	
Nurses' station	40-60 NSF/seat	80 NSF minimum
Receptionist workstation	50-70 NSF/receptionist	
Clerical workstation	60 NSF/secretary (without files)* 80 NSF/secretary (with files)*	
Conference room	20 NSF/seat	100 NSF minimum
Classroom	12-15 NSF/seat	120 NSF minimum
Film viewing area	40 NSF/viewing station	
Office: 1 technician	80-100 NSF	
Office: 1 staff member	80-120 NSF	
Office: 2 staff members	140-180 NSF	
Office: 1 director	100-150 NSF	
Staff lounge	15 NSF/seat	80 NSF minimum
Staff locker	Full-height: 7 NSF/person (includes changing area)* Half-height: 5 NSF/person* Purse box: 3 NSF/person*	60 NSF minimum.
Staff shower	20 NSF/shower (not handicapped-accessible)	Consult applicable codes for handicapped accessibility requirements.

(continued)

Table 3. Space Determinants of Selected Support and Administrative Spaces (continued)

Area Description	Space Programming Guidelines	Remarks
Toilets: Non-handicapped-accessible	30 NSF/1 toilet & 1 lavatory Assume 2 toilets/15,000 annual primary care visits*	Consult applicable codes for handicapped accessibility requirements (see "Handicapped-accessible toilets," below).
Toilets: Handicapped-accessible	46 NSF (minimum)/1 toilet & 1 lavatory	Consult applicable codes for handicapped accessibility requirements.
Patient dressing cubicle	15 NSF (minimum)/non-handicapped-accessible dressing cubicle	May be located within exam-treatment room. Consult applicable codes for handicapped accessibility requirements.
Patient locker	3-7 NSF/exam-treatment room	See "Staff locker" remarks, above.
Stretcher holding alcove	18 NSF/stretcher	
Wheelchair holding alcove	4 NSF/folded wheelchair	
Public telephone alcove	10 NSF/telephone	
Janitor's closet	24-40 NSF/closet	
Scrub station	15-20 NSF/sink at dedicated scrub alcove	Required NSF per sink may be reduced if sinks are recessed along circulation corridors. Consult applicable codes for required number of scrub sinks.
Clean supply room	15 NSF/primary care procedure room* 10 NSF/surgical recovery bed*	
Soiled holding room	10 NSF/primary care procedure room* 5 NSF/surgical recovery bed*	

*Adapted from *Evaluation and Space Programming Methodologies.* Canada: Minister of Health and Welfare, 1984.

Table 4. Minimum Space Requirements for Basic Two-Room Operating Room Suite

Room or Area	No. of Rooms	Unit Size NSM†	Unit Size (NSF)	Total NSM	Total (NSF)
Surgical Suite					
General operating room	2	37	(400)	74	(800)
Case cart storage	1	11	(120)	11	(120)
Anesthesia workroom/storage	1	11	(120)	11	(120)
Clean/sterile supplies	1	11	(120)	11	(120)
Control room/clerical	1	1.4	(150)	14	(150)
Dictation	1	2.0	(20)	2.0	(20)
Equipment storage	1	7.5	(80)	7.5	(80)
Anesthesia gas storage	1	4.0	(40)	4.0	(40)
Janitor's closet	2	3.0	(30)	6.0	(60)
Pre-op patient holding	1	8.5	(90)	8.5	(90)
Scrub area	2	4.5	(50)	9.5	(100)
Soiled holding	1	9.5	(100)	9.5	(100)
Stretcher holding	1	4.5	(50)	4.5	(50)
Recovery Area					
Beds for ambulatory observation	4	7.5	(80)	30	(320)
Clean utility	1	6.5	(70)	6.5	(70)
Isolation bed	1	15	(160)	15	(160)
Nursing station	1	7.5	(80)	7.5	(80)
Soiled utility	1	4.5	(50)	4.5	(50)
Staff lockers (men)	1	5.5	(60)	5.5	(60)
Staff lockers (women)	1	5.5	(60)	5.5	(60)
Staff lounge	1	7.5	(80)	7.5	(80)
Anesthetist's office*	1	11	(120)	11	(120)
Head nurse's office	1	9.5	(100)	9.5	(100)
Total net space				275	(2,950)
Net-to-gross conversion factor		×1.4			
Departmental gross space				385	(4,130)

*Optional.   †Net square meters

Source: *Evaluation and Space Programming Methodologies.* Canada: Minister of Health and Welfare, 1984, p. 20.5. Reprinted with the permission of Health and Welfare, Ottawa, Canada.

Appendix C

Facility Layout Guidelines

Source: Adapted from *The Medical Facility: Equipment and Supplies.* DHEW publication #HSA 75-15016, 1975.

What Kind of a Facility Do You Need?

The kind of medical facility needed is one that will accommodate the type of medical services the owner has decided will be delivered, and it should be designed with this in mind. For example, if the practice expects to have two physicians providing general medical services, and if the practice will include limited laboratory and x-ray procedures, then the facility should ideally have space for the following:

• Examination rooms
• Consulting rooms
• Waiting room
• Nurses' station
• Small laboratory
• X-ray room
• Lavatories
• Storage room
• Reception/business/medical record room

Keep in mind that some states dictate prescribed specifications for a medical facility, such as size and number of examination rooms. Check with the comprehensive health planning agency in your locale to determine whether your state has special facility requirements.

Should You Renovate, Lease, or Build Your Facility?

Once the decisions have been made on the general specifications of your facility, the owner must determine whether to renovate, lease, or build the facility. This decision will depend on several factors:

• Desired location
• Financial resources
• Availability of buildings with the necessary potential for renovation

Where Should the Facility Be Located?

The location of your medical practice determines to a large degree the number of people who will use it. People tend to use facilities that are accessible and convenient. If you have several options available to you, the selection should be the site which is located in the most densely populated portion of the area to be served by the facility. An example of this is the business area of the county seat or some other center of community activity. Points to consider include the following:

- Accessibility to roads and public transportation
- Proximity to other health care resources (hospital, dental services, nursing home)
- Suitable terrain (adequate drainage, easy accessibility in snow or rain)
- Local zoning requirements
- County or municipal building codes and utility requirements
- Availability of water, sewer service, electricity, fuel, and garbage disposal
- Adequate space for parking

In selecting a facility location, consider one that will present the fewest transportation problems for handicapped patients. In addition, if the facility is located above or below street level, there should always be an elevator or a ramp for the use of handicapped patients and/or staff.

In all cases, your practice should be clearly identified by an outside sign and sufficient outdoor lighting so that potential patients are aware of its location.

Remember that there are resources available to assist in planning the facility. Some of these resources are:

- The local medical society
- The community health planning agency in your area
- Health facility architects

How Should the Interior Be Designed?

The facility should be designed to provide efficient use of the available space and at the same time provide an attractive environment for patients and staff.

When designing the interior of your facility, the following areas should be given special attention and all considerations should be discussed thoroughly before final decisions are made.

Waiting Area

- Location of the waiting area should be immediately inside the front entrance so that the receptionist can see patients as they arrive and leave.
- Comfortable and sufficient seating should be available for waiting patients. As a rule of thumb, the minimum should be two seats per examination room.
- Space should be provided for a coat rack.
- Enough space should be allowed for children's quiet activities. This space might have a small table, chairs, and some children's books.

Receptionist and Business Area

- The area should be easily accessible to both patients and staff.
- The area should be located in a manner that allows the receptionist to clearly view the waiting patients.
- The area should be convenient to the provider's work area to facilitate communication and supervision of (1) patient traffic, (2) flow of medical records, and (3) billing information.
- Space for medical record storage should be convenient to the receptionist or appointment clerk's work area.
- Enough working area should be given to the receptionist to allow

performance of tasks with maximum efficiency. The usual amount of space allowed for this purpose is 60 square feet per individual working in the area.
- If possible, a separate space or room should be near the receptionist/business area to allow for private discussion related to registration or billing questions.
- In larger offices it may be advantageous to have separate areas or windows for reception and payments.

Examination Rooms and Consultation Rooms

This section of your facility should form a well-integrated unit. Each room should provide complete privacy for patients and yet be easily accessible to providers.

- Examination/treatment rooms. The number, size, and design of these depends largely on the number of patients seen and the types of service available at the practice. As a rule of thumb, a minimum of two examination/treatment rooms per provider is needed. The size of the examination/treatment room is important. If too small, the provider may not have enough space around the examination table to comfortably perform some procedures; if too large, patients are likely to feel a lack of privacy. A good space allotment for an examination/treatment room is 9 feet by 11 feet. Pediatric examination rooms are often a little smaller. At least one examination/treatment room should have a door wide enough to permit entrance of a stretcher patient or wheelchair (3 feet 8 inches). All applicable codes should be reviewed in making size determinations.

- Consultation rooms (physicians' offices). Each provider needs a private office in which to consult with patients and other providers, as well as to conduct the normal business of the practice. In most cases, this room does not have to be very large. It should have enough space for a desk, bookcases, and chairs (approximately 100 square feet). For practices in which the majority of patients complete their visit in the consultation room, it should be located between the examination area and the waiting room. Frequently, limited space may require the consultation area to be combined with one of the examination/ treatment rooms. Such a combination room should be at least 120 square feet.

Lavatories

The number of lavatories needed in your facility will depend on the expected size of your practice. However, every facility needs at least one lavatory. Easy access to the lavatory is very important, both for persons waiting and for patients being treated. Some states require two lavatories in the facility in order to qualify for provider status. Consult all applicable codes and accreditation standards.

- If laboratory work is done on the premises, a lavatory should be located next to it. A shuttered pass-through window for specimens is desirable.
- Ideally, a staff lavatory should also be provided.

Other Work Areas

Other work areas in a clinic might include laboratory, x-ray, and utility/ storage.

- Laboratory. To save steps, this room should be centrally located relative to the examination rooms and lavatories.
- Utility room(s). Because most of the soiled linen and supplies are kept in this room, it should be easily accessible from the examination/ treatment rooms.
- X-ray room. Special shielding accommodations must be made because of the dangers of radiation. If you plan to have x-ray equipment at your clinic, you should speak to the distributor of that equipment about location, electrical wiring, and lead shielding. Health departments in many jurisdictions have a physicist available to advise you on x-ray shielding requirements.

Corridors and Traffic Areas

Another consideration in a well-organized office is the design of the traffic areas.

- Corridors should be wide enough for two-way traffic. (Consult all applicable codes.)
- Traffic areas should not be obstructed by equipment and supplies.
- Corridor space should not be used for storage under any circumstances.
- Remember that fire regulations require that all doors open into rooms and not into the corridors. This will also ensure patients' privacy in examination rooms.

Parking Space

Off-street parking is preferred. Adequate parking for both staff and patients should be available.

How Should The Interior Be Finished?

Once agreement has been reached regarding basic interior design, decisions should be made on the interior fixtures and materials. Careful attention should be paid to such things as the lighting, floor covering, plumbing fixtures, and acoustics.

Lighting

Medical and work areas require good overhead lighting. The waiting room should have lighting suitable for reading. Entrances and parking areas should be well lighted.

Floor Covering

Carpeting is desirable for the reception area and corridors. Lavatories and examination rooms should have a smooth surface that can be easily and frequently cleaned and disinfected.

Plumbing Fixtures

Each examination room, and the laboratory, should have a sink equipped with wrist-action faucets and a gooseneck spout. Consult all applicable codes and accreditation standards.

Acoustical Considerations

Patient privacy is a primary consideration. Examination rooms, consultation rooms and any areas where confidential medical information is discussed should be adequately soundproofed so that these conversations will not be overheard in the waiting area or the adjacent examination room.

Appendix D

Resources

This bibliographic list directs the reader to more information about many of the topics discussed in the text. In addition to these resources, information can also be obtained from professional and trade associations, equipment manufacturers, and specialty libraries such as those affiliated with medical schools and schools of architecture.

This list is subdivided by subject area, in alphabetical order, and covers the following categories: ambulatory surgery facilities; anthropometric design data; architectural contracts; architectural programming; barrier-free design; building codes, regulations, and standards; color in architecture; construction cost analysis; emergicenter facilities; health care architects, consultants, and associations; health care facilities (general); site selection and site analysis; and terminology.

Ambulatory Surgery Facilities

American College of Surgeons. Ambulatory surgery: When and what procedures. *Bulletin, American College of Surgeons.* 1982 Nov. 67 (11):21-23.

American Medical Association. *Establishing Freestanding Ambulatory Surgery Centers: The Planning and Regulatory Process.* Chicago: AMA, 1982.

Badner, B. "Outpatient Surgery Facilities," in: *Hospital Special Care Facilities: Planning for User Needs.* Harold Laufman, ed. New York City: Academic Press, 1981, pp. 407-414.

Beck, W.C. Operating room illumination: The current state of the art. *Bulletin, American College of Surgeons.* 1981 May. 66(5):10-15.

Berkoff, M. Planning and designing ambulatory surgery facilities. *Journal of Ambulatory Care Management.* 1981 Aug. 4(3):35-51.

Brengande, B.J. Modular units offer design flexibility. *Hospitals, J.A.H.A.* 1975 Oct. 1. 49:66-69.

Bowles, C. Ambulatory surgery: Considerations in planning. *Medical Group Management.* 1981 Jan.-Feb. 28(1):60-65.

Brinkman, B. Experienced manager shares tips on outpatient facility design. *Same Day Surgery.* 1981 Jul. 5(7):85-6.

Burn, J. Facility design for outpatient surgery and anesthesia. *International Anesthesiology Clinic.* 1982 Spring. 20(1):135-51.

Burns, L., ed. *Ambulatory Surgery Centers.* Rockville, MD: Aspen Systems, 1983.

Edwards, B. How to set up an efficient outpatient recovery room. *Same Day Surgery.* 1981 May. 5(5):60-62.

Ford, J.L. Outpatient surgery: Present status and future projections. *Medical Journal.* 1978 Mar. 71(3):311-15.

Freestanding Ambulatory Surgery Association. *State Ambulatory Surgery Center Survey.* Alexandria, VA: FASA, 1985.

Good, R., and Greensher, A., eds. *Guide to Ambulatory Surgery.* Orlando, FL: Grune & Stratton, Inc., 1982.

Goodspeed, S. Planning, developing, and implementing a freestanding ambulatory surgery center. *Health Care Strategic Management.* 1986 Feb. 4(2):18-22.

Grossman, R. Is ambulatory surgery less expensive? *Hospitals.* 1979 May 16. 53:112-16.

Grubb, R.D., and Ondov, G. *Planning Ambulatory Surgery Facilities.* St. Louis, MO: C.V. Mosby Company, 1979.

Hejna, W., and Gutman, C. *Management of Surgical Facilities.* Rockville, MD: Aspen Systems, Inc., 1984.

Kempe, A.R., and Gelazis, R. Patient anxiety levels: An ambulatory surgery study. *AORN Journal.* 1985 Feb. 41(2):390-96.

Klebanoff, G. Operating room design: An introduction. *Bulletin, American College of Surgeons.* 1979 Nov. 64(11):6-10.

Minister of Health and Welfare, Canada. *Evaluation and Space Programming Methodologies,* Surgery/Day Surgery, ch. 20. Canada: MHW, 1984.

O'Donovan, T., ed. *Ambulatory Surgical Centers: Development and Management.* Rockville, MD: Aspen Systems, Inc., 1984.

Reed, W.A., and Ford, J.L. The surgicenter: An ambulatory surgical facility. *Clinical Obstetrics and Gynecology.* 1974 Sept. 17(3):217-29.

Riffer, J. Freestanding emergency and surgery centers. *Hospitals.* 1984 Dec. 16. 58:50.

Ryan, J. *A Bibliography of the Operating Room Environment (1973-1983 cumulation).* Chicago: American College of Surgeons, 1984, pp. 39-48.

Traska, M. Surgery center prototype works well in Tucson. *Modern Health Care.* 1978 Aug. 8:40-41.

Trivedi, V., and Williams, S.J. Planning and decision making for ambulatory surgery. *Journal of Medical Systems.* 1980 4(3-4):327-45.

Anthropometric Design Data

Callender, J.H., ed. *Time Saver Standards for Architectural Design Data,* 6th ed. New York City: McGraw-Hill, 1982.

Packard, R.T., ed. *Architectural Graphic Standards,* 7th ed. New York City: John Wiley & Sons, 1981.

Panero, J. *Anatomy for Interior Designers,* 3rd ed. New York City: Whitney Library of Design, 1962.

Panero, J., and Zelnick, M. *Human Dimensions and Interior Space: A Sourcebook of Design Reference Standards.* New York City: Whitney Library of Design, 1979.

Architectural Contracts

Acret, J. *Architects and Engineers: Their Professional Responsibilities.* New York City: McGraw-Hill, 1977.

American Institute of Architects. *The Architect's Handbook of Professional Practice,* vols. 1-3. Washington, DC: AIA, 1985.

American Institute of Architects. *Standard Form of Agreement between Owner and Architect.* AIA document B141. Washington, DC: AIA, 1977.

Greenstreet, B., and Greenstreet, K. *The Architect's Guide to Law and Practice.* New York City: Van Nostrand Reinhold, 1984.

Hauf, H.D. *Building Contracts for Design and Construction,* 2nd ed. New York City: John Wiley & Sons, 1976.

Hohns, M. *Deskbook of Construction Contract Law with Forms.* Englewood Cliffs, NJ: Prentice-Hall, Inc., 1981.

Murvin, H.L. *The Architect's Responsibilities in the Project Delivery Process,* 2nd ed. Oakland, CA: H.L. Murvin, 1982.

Spencer, Whalen, and Graham. *AIA Building Construction Legal Citator,* rev. ed. Washington, DC: AIA, 1980.

Sweet, J. *Legal Aspects of Architecture, Engineering, and the Construction Process.* St. Paul, MN: West Publishing Co., 1977.

Tomson, B., and Coplan, N. *Architectural and Engineering Law,* 2nd ed. New York City: Van Nostrand Reinhold, 1967.

Architectural Programming

(See also Building Codes, Regulations, and Standards, below)

Chi Systems, Inc. *Evaluation and Space Programming Methodology Series.* Ann Arbor, MI: Chi Systems, Inc., 1978-81. (*See* Minister of Health and Welfare, Canada.)

Coleman, J.R., and Kaminsky, F.C. Sizing free-standing ambulatory care facilities. *Journal of Ambulatory Care Management.* 1979 Nov. 2(4):1-19.

Hayward, C., and others (members of the Committee on Architecture for Health). *A Generic Process for Projecting Health Care Space Needs.* Washington, DC: American Institute of Architects, 1985.

Marti, M. Jr. *Space Operational Analysis.* West Lafayette, IN: PDA Publishers Corporation, 1981.

Minister of Health and Welfare, Canada. *Evaluation and Space Programming Methodologies.* Canada: MHW, 1984. (Also published as *Evaluation... Methodology Series,* 1978-81.)

Palmer, M.A. *The Architect's Guide to Facility Programming.* Washington, DC: American Institute of Architects, 1981.

Peña, W. *Problem Seeking: An Architectural Programming Primer.* Houston, TX: Cahners Books International, 1977.

U.S. Department of Health, Education and Welfare. *The Health Maintenance Organization Facility Development Handbook.* Washington, DC: USDHEW, 1975.

Barrier-Free Design

In addition to consulting local codes, standards, and regulations, the following resources may be helpful.

American National Standards Institute, Inc. *Providing Accessibility and Usability for Physically Handicapped People.* (ANSI A 117.1-1986) New York City: ANSI, 1986.

American Society of Landscape Architects. *Barrier-Free Site Design.* Washington, DC: U.S. Department of Housing and Urban Development, 1975.

Lynch, R. *Easy Access: A Digest of the Requirements of the New ANSI Standards.* Scottsdale, AZ: Robert Lynch, 1982.

Building Codes, Regulations, and Standards

Before specific codes are researched extensively, a regulatory survey should be done to determine whose jurisdiction a particular project falls under and therefore which codes will govern. These codes may include the following:

- Local codes
- Model codes
- Building codes, such as the Uniform Building Code, Basic Building Code, National Building Code, and Southern Building Code
- Specialty codes covering such areas as fire safety (for example, the Life Safety Code), electric work, plumbing, and others

After the applicable codes, standards, and regulations have been identified, the building's *occupancy classification* should be determined to identify which parts of the applicable code will govern. For example, the following classifications—Ambulatory Health Care, Nonambulatory Health Care, and Business Occupancy—have different requirements.

American Medical Association. *Establishing Freestanding Ambulatory Surgery Centers: The Planning and Regulatory Process.* Chicago: AMA, 1982.

Correale, W.H. *A Building Code Primer.* New York City: McGraw-Hill, 1979.

Goldberg, A. *Design Guide to the 1985 Uniform Building Code.* Mill Valley, CA: Grda Press, 1985.

Hageman, J.M. *Contractor's Guide to the Building Code.* Carlsbad, CA: Craftsman Book Co., 1983.

International Conference of Building Officials. *Uniform Building Code.* Whittier, CA: ICBO, 1985.

Joint Commission on Accreditation of Hospitals. *Accreditation Manual for Ambulatory Care.* Chicago: JCAH, 1986.

Klein, B.F. *Health Care Facilities Handbook.* Quincy, MA: National Fire Protection Association, 1984.

Lathrop, J.K., ed. *Life Safety Code Handbook,* 2nd ed. Quincy, MA: National Fire Protection Association, 1985.

National Fire Protection Association. *Life Safety Code 1985.* NFPA 101. Quincy, MA: NFPA, 1985.

National Fire Protection Association. *Health Care Facilities 1984.* NFPA 99. Quincy, MA: NFPA, 1985.

U.S. Department of Health and Human Services. *Minimum Requirements for Construction and Equipment of Hospital and Medical Facilities.* Washington, DC: Public Health Service, Health Resources and Services Administration, 1982.

Color in Architecture

Birren, F. Human response to color and light. *Hospitals.* 1979 Jul. 16. 53:93-96.

Birren, F. *Light, Color, and Environment: A Discussion of the Biological and Psychological Effects of Color.* New York City: Van Nostrand Reinhold, 1982.

Carpman, J., and others. *Design That Cares: Planning Health Facilities for Patients and Visitors.* Chicago: American Hospital Publishing, Inc., 1986, pp. 76, 172, 229.

Malkin, J. *The Design of Medical and Dental Facilities.* New York City: Van Nostrand Reinhold, 1982, chapters 9 and 14.

National Bureau of Standards. *Color in the Health Care Environment.* U.S. Department of Commerce, 1978.

Construction Cost Analysis

Dell'Isola, A., and Kirk, S.J. *Life-Cycle Costing for Design Professionals.* New York City: McGraw-Hill, 1981.

Dell'Isola, A., and Kirk, S.J. *Life Cycle Cost Data.* New York City: McGraw-Hill, 1982.

Haviland, D.S., ed. *Life Cycle Cost Analysis: A Guide for Architects.* Washington, DC: American Institute of Architects, 1977.

Haviland, D.S. *Life Cycle Cost Analysis 2: Using It in Practice.* Washington, DC: American Institute of Architects, 1977.

Means Building Construction Cost Data. Kingston, MA: Robert Snow Means Co., 1985 (An annual publication).

Means Interior Cost Data: Partitions, Ceilings, Finishes, Floors, Furnishings. Kingston, MA: Robert Snow Means Co., 1985 (An annual publication).

Means Square Foot Costs: Residential, Commercial, Industrial, Institutional. Kingston, MA: Robert Snow Means Co., 1985 (An annual publication).

Means Systems Costs. Kingston, MA: Robert Snow Means Co., 1985 (An annual publication).

Pereira, P.E., ed. *Special Dodge Report: Hospital/Healthcare Building Costs 1986.* New York City: McGraw-Hill, 1986.

Pereira, P.E. *Dodge Construction Systems Costs 1985.* New York City: McGraw-Hill, 1986.

Swinburne, H. *Design Cost Analysis for Architects and Engineers.* New York City: McGraw-Hill, 1980.

Emergicenter Facilities

American Medical Association. *Report of the American Medical Association Board of Trustees: Freestanding Emergency Medical Care Centers.* Chicago: AMA, 1983.

Burns, L.A., and Ferber, M.S. Freestanding emergency care center creates public policy issues. *Hospitals.* 1981 May 16. 55:73-75.

Drury, L.R., and Rosen, P. Multiple use, flexibility, key emergency department planning. *Hospitals, J.A.H.A.* 1977 Jul. 16. 51:201-11.

Freestanding emergency unit designed for expansion. *Hospitals.* 1981 Apr. 16. 55:35-40.

Kaplan, A.S., and others. Freestanding emergency clinics: Community development guidelines. *Annals of Emergency Medicine.* 1981 Jun. 10(6):318-23.

Katz, C. Free-standing treatment centers: Another member of the competition. *Postgraduate Medicine.* 1983 Aug. 74(2):291-94.

Koncel, J.A. Experts examine major issues facing emergicenters. *Hospitals.* 1981 May 16. 55:83-90.

Plant, J. The urgent care craze. *Hospitals.* 1983 Jun. 57:25, 26, 28-31.

Powills, S. Freestanding emergency center experts outline equipment staffing needs; ailments seen. *Hospitals.* 1985 May 16. 59:44.

Powills, S. Three factors for freestanding emergency center success cited: Location, location, location. *Hospitals.* 1985 May 16. 59:46.

Riffer, J. Freestanding emergency and surgery centers. *Hospitals.* 1984 Dec. 16. 58:50.

Seager, S., and Barber, B. Hospital and its freestanding emergency facilities form network. *Hospitals.* 1981 May 16. 55:79-81.

Shiver, J.M.; Jacobs, W.F. Jr.; and Cassidy, W.J. Center provides emergency care without unneeded inpatient units. *Hospitals, J.A.H.A.* 1979 Apr. 16. 53:116-19.

Health Care Architects, Consultants, and Associations

Publications

Directory of Planning and Design for Health Care Facilities. Chicago: American Hospital Association, 1986.

Nackel, J.G., and others. *Working with Health Care Consultants.* Chicago: American Hospital Publishing, Inc., 1986.

Schirmer, H.W. *Profile: The Official AIA Directory of Architectural Firms.* New York City: Van Nostrand Reinhold, 1980.

Associations

American Association for Hospital Planning
1101 Connecticut Avenue N.W., Suite 700
Washington, DC 20036

American Association of Hospital Consultants
1235 Jefferson Davis Highway, #602
Arlington, VA 22202

American Hospital Association
840 North Lake Shore Drive
Chicago, IL 60611

American Institute of Architects Committee on Architecture for Health
1735 New York Avenue N.W.
Washington, DC 20006

Joint Commission on Accreditation of Hospitals
875 North Michigan Avenue
Chicago, IL 60611

Health Care Facilities (General)

Allen, R.W., and von Karolyi, I. *Hospital Planning Handbook.* New York City: John Wiley & Sons, 1976.

American Hospital Association. *Signs and Graphics for Health Care Facilities.* Chicago: American Hospital Publishing, Inc., 1979.

American Medical Association. *Planning Guide for Physician's Medical Facilities,* 2nd ed. Chicago: AMA, 1975.

Arizona Statewide Health Coordinating Council. *Arizona State Health Plan, 1982-1987.* Phoenix, AZ: Arizona Department of Health Services, 1982.

Arneill, B.P. Guidelines for design of facilities. *Hospitals, J.A.H.A.* 1975 Apr. 16. 49:83-87.

Arneill, B.P. The planning and design process for ambulatory care facilities. *Journal of Ambulatory Care Management.* 1978 Jan. 1(1):75-87.

Burgen, A.J. Construction considerations for ambulatory care facilities. *Hospitals, J.A.H.A.* 1976 Feb. 50:79-84.

Carpman, J., and others. *Design That Cares: Planning Health Facilities for Patients and Visitors.* Chicago: American Hospital Publishing, Inc., 1986.

College of American Pathologists, Laboratory Function and Design Committee. *Medical Laboratory Planning and Design.* Skokie, IL: CAP, 1985.

Committee on Department Planning, Commission on Radiologic Equipment and Facilities. *Planning Guide for Radiologic Installations, Fascicle 4: Basic Concepts.* Chicago, IL: American College of Radiology, 1977, p. 31.

Fleming, R. Design of outpatient areas. *Hospital Topics.* 1973 Oct. 51(5):46.

Garrett, R.P. *Hospitals—A Systems Approach.* Philadelphia: Auerbach Publishers, Inc., 1973.

Giglio, R. *Ambulatory Care Systems, Vol II: Location, Layout and Information Systems for Efficient Operations.* Lexington, MA: Lexington Books, 1977.

Green, A.C. Changes in care call for design flexibility. *Hospitals, J.A.H.A.* 1976 Feb. 1. 50:67-69.

Hardy, O.B., and Lammers, L.P. *Hospitals: The Planning and Design Process,* 2nd ed. Rockville, MD: Aspen Systems Corp., 1986.

Kanaan, G.E. *Parking and Access for General Hospitals.* Westport, CT: Eno Foundation, 1983.

Malkin, J. *The Design of Medical and Dental Facilities.* New York City: Van Nostrand Reinhold, 1982.

Meshenberg, K.A., and Burns, L.A., eds. *Hospital Ambulatory Care: Making It Work.* Chicago: American Hospital Publishing, Inc., 1983.

Mills, A.P., ed. *Functional Planning of General Hospitals.* New York City: McGraw-Hill, 1969.

National Health Service Corps. *The Medical Facility: Equipment and Supplies.* Washington, DC: USDHEW, 1975.

Panther, R. Hospital design in 2015. *Hospital Forum.* 1985 Jul.-Aug. 28(4):27-30.

Parker, W. Jr. Flexible designs are key to reuse projects. *Hospitals, J.A.H.A.* 1979 Feb. 16. 53:125-84.

Porter, D.R. *Hospital Architecture: Guidelines for Design and Renovation.* Ann Arbor, MI: AUPHA Press, 1982.

Pütsep, E. *Modern Hospital.* London: Lloyd-Luke Ltd., 1974.

Quebe, J.L. The changing landscape of healthcare. *Health Care Strategic Management.* 1985 Dec. 3(12):4-10.

Rea, J.; Frommelt, J.J.; and MacCoun, M.D. *Building a Hospital: A Primer for Administrators.* Chicago: American Hospital Publishing, Inc., 1978.

Redstone, L.G., ed. *Hospitals and Health Care Facilities: An Architectural Record Book,* 2nd ed. New York City: McGraw-Hill, 1978.

Rising, E.J. *Ambulatory Care Systems, Vol I: Design for Improved Patient Flow.* Lexington, MA: Lexington Books, 1977.

Shannon, W.R. Architecture for group practice: Master plan by design. *Group Practice.* 1970 Nov. 19(6):20-23.

Shannon, W.R. Medical group practice architecture, design and function. *New Horizons in Health Care: First International Congress of Group Medicine.* 1970 Apr. 26-30. 1:207-19.

Sprague, J.G. How to get health facilities built. *Hospitals, J.A.H.A.* 1976 Feb. 1. 50:73-78.

Sprague, J.G. The need for ambulatory care facilities. *Hospitals J.A.H.A.* 1976 Feb. 1. 50:58-59.

Toland, D., and Strong, S. *Hospital-Based Medical Office Buildings,* 2nd ed. Chicago: American Hospital Publishing, Inc., 1986.

Site Selection and Site Analysis

Lifton, J., and Hardy, O.B. *Site Selection for Health Care Facilities.* Chicago: American Hospital Publishing, Inc., 1982.

White, E.T. *Site Analysis: Diagramming Information for Architectural Design.* Tucson, AZ: Architectural Media, 1983.

De Chiara, J., and Koppelman, L.E. *Site Planning Standards.* New York City: McGraw-Hill, 1978.

Terminology

Kiger, A.F., ed. *Hospital Administration Terminology,* 2nd ed. Chicago: American Hospital Publishing, Inc., 1986.

Construction Specifications Institute. *A Glossary of Construction Specifications Terminology.* Washington, DC: CSI, 1981.

Cowan, H.J. *Dictionary of Architectural Science.* New York City: Halsted Press, 1973.

Institute for Health Planning. *Glossary of Health Care Delivery and Planning Terms.* Madison, WI: IHP, 1981.

National Association of Women in Construction. *Construction Dictionary: Construction Terms and Tables.* Phoenix, AZ: NAWC, 1981.

Means Illustrated Construction Dictionary. New York City: McGraw-Hill, 1985.